The first Mechanics' Institute in London was founded in 1823 by George Birkbeck. "Mechanics" then meant skilled artisans, and the purpose of the Institute was to instruct them in the principles behind their craft. The Institute became Birkbeck College, part of London University, in 1920 but still maintains one foot in the academy and one in the outside world.

NO. 16

THE MECHANICS'
INSTITUTE REVIEW

AUTUMN 2019
THE CLIMATE ISSUE

THE MECHANICS' INSTITUTE REVIEW is published by MA Creative Writing, Department of English and Humanities, School of Arts, Birkbeck, Malet Street, Bloomsbury, London WC1E 7HX englishandhumanities@bbk.ac.uk

ISBN 978-1-9999622-2-7

PROJECT DIRECTOR
Julia Bell

MANAGING EDITOR
Sue Tyley

EDITORIAL TEAM
Claire Blakemore, Karen Clarke, Eman Elabdi, Niamh Fitzgerald, Charlotte Forfieh, Shaniqua Harris, Catriona Knox, Lou Kramskoy, Elizabeth Lovatt, Denise McCulloch, Nicolau Sultanum

DESIGNER
Mark Cortes Favis,
LO/LA Design

PHOTO EDITOR
Michael Radford

The Editorial Team would like to thank Julia Bell and Sue Tyley, for making this project possible; Hannah Copley, for her poetry advice; and Melanie Jones, for managing submissions and data. Also our readers: Liz Bolton, Angèle Chevalier, Stephanie Heyes, Aiden Morris, and Tamara Pollock.

THE MECHANICS' INSTITUTE REVIEW is distributed by NBNi and represented by Inpress Books

Printed and bound in the UK

mironline.org

CONTENTS

NO. 16
AUTUMN 2019
THE CLIMATE ISSUE

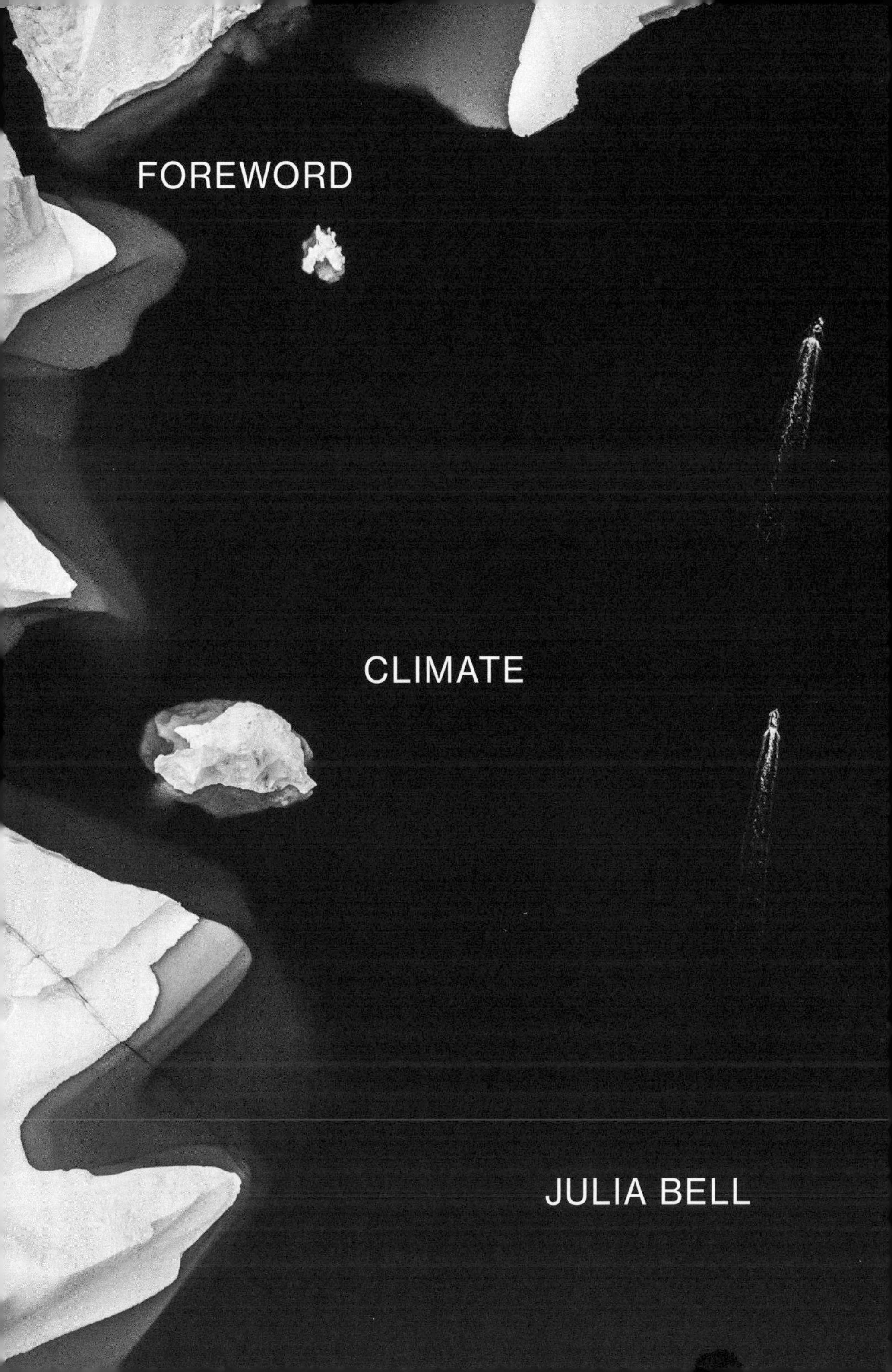

FOREWORD

CLIMATE

JULIA BELL

I n this latest issue of *The Mechanics' Institute Review*, the journal of new writing produced and edited by the Birkbeck creative writing programme, we have both widened our open call for submissions, by including poetry and essays as well as short-form fiction, and sharpened its focus, by asking the authors to respond to a theme. We invited our writers to consider ideas of Climate. Not only *the* climate – which we know is under pressure from the pollution of human activity – but the climate more generally, the ideological, political, sociological, emotional atmosphere in which we all live and breathe.

Climate is not the weather, but the weather is the effect of climate. If the climate is impacted by our pollution it follows that our environment will be degraded; if our environment is degraded it follows that species loss and extreme weather events will be the consequence. If climate is the abstract noun, the changing weather patterns are the observed reality. And to take the point further, if we live in a climate of fear, it then follows that the weather will evidence violence, anxiety, apprehension.

Writers are good at reading the weather. It's what they are trained to do – pay attention to the small stuff, that which shows, not tells, bigger truths. The contributors to this volume have each responded to the idea of climate in their own way, from personal narratives about the persecution of academics, to imagining strange new dystopias, to documenting austerity, or exploring established narratives of culpability and innocence.

We encouraged authors to engage with the theme of Climate in its broadest possible terms, not just to focus on the science, but to reflect on how the current climate makes us feel and think, how we might act in such uncertain times. To make poems and stories in response; to *do*. This anthology aims to provide a platform for a conversation. There is still a dark culture of denial around matters of climate in the political sphere. Those who would deny the changes are often shills for the corporations whose livelihoods depend on such a conversation not happening. Denial is also one of the classic stages of grief, one of the inevitable paths that we must navigate to arrive at some acceptance of loss. This issue of *The Mechanics' Institute Review* is a hedge against loss, an opportunity for a conversation, an invitation to think, to engage, to participate, not just with fear and grief, but with hope and humour too. With lyric and character and description and story – with language; it's all we've got.

Julia Bell
Birkbeck, 2019

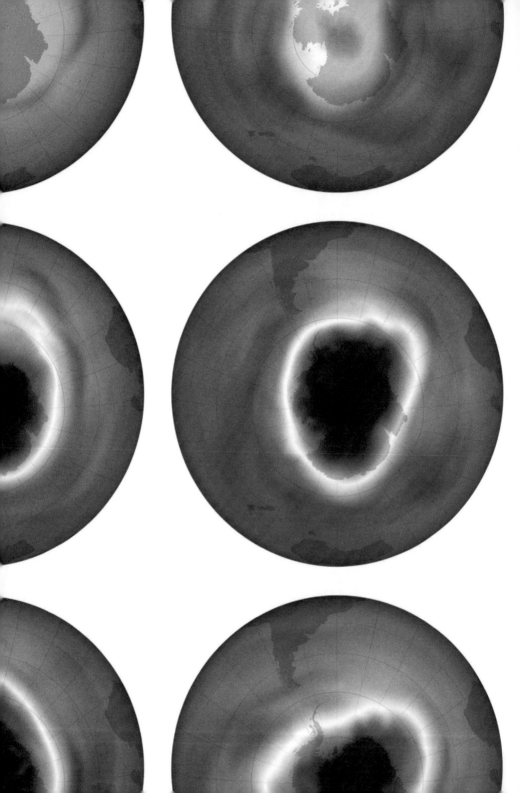

NON-FICTION

HOW MUCH
ARE THEY
PAYING YOU?

RICHARD HAMBLYN

Somewhere on my office floor lies a much-hurled copy of *State of Fear* (2004), Michael Crichton's swivel-eyed conspiracy thriller in which global warming – as it used to be called – is exposed as an elaborate scientific fraud, contrived by corrupt environmentalists as a means of prolonging their funding. The novel is brilliantly, if loopily, inventive, not least in its appropriation of a scholarly apparatus including footnotes, appendices and an annotated bibliography: imagine a doctoral thesis crayoned by Donald Trump. But even Crichton's most devoted readers must have been surprised to see him called before the United States Senate as an expert witness on climate change. According to James Inhofe, the Republican Senator responsible for inviting him, anthropogenic climate change remains "the greatest hoax ever perpetrated", a sentiment endorsed by a number of the energy companies that have funded Inhofe's campaigns over the years, though not, of course, by any of the climate scientists whose work was examined at the hearing.[1] Crichton was only too happy to second the Senator's views, dismissing the "so-called" scientific consensus on atmospheric warming, while hinting that climate scientists are motivated by the thought that their continued funding depends on upholding the politically mainstream view.

The image of scientists as a herd of compliant sheep plodding after grant allocations has become a powerful missile in the climate sceptics' armoury. The idea that academics are in it for the money is surprisingly prevalent, and would be falling-over funny if it wasn't for the political edge, the hint of threat, that so often turns the imputation into a weapon.

I've had a taste of this weaponry myself. A few years ago, I was commissioned to write some public-facing material for the Met Office, notably *The Cloud Book: How to Understand the Skies* (2008), which outlined the major families of clouds, and their varying influence on weather and climate; and then a follow-up volume, entitled *Extraordinary Clouds* (2009), which introduced some of the weird and wonderful cloud formations that fail to sit securely within the official classification. It's surprising how many clouds, especially human-made ones, remain meteorological outliers. But it was in the course of that second Met Office volume that I made the mistake of mentioning "chemtrails", the subject of a widespread conspiracy theory that claims aircraft contrails (also known as vapour trails) are formed not from water and particulates present in aircraft exhaust plumes, but are in fact the deliberate products of a covert, global geoengineering programme. According to the theory, the conspiracy involves chemical spraying of the Earth's upper atmosphere for a host of nefarious purposes, ranging from weather modification, particularly the deliberate dimming of the sky, to genetic engineering of crops and diseases, the development of electromagnetic super-weapons, population reduction, even political mind control, all of which has led to devastating ecological and health consequences around the world. It is, in every sense, an extraordinary claim.

In the book, I had written in passing that there is no evidence for the chemtrail theory, and that aircraft contrails, although human-made, behave like natural cirrus clouds as soon as they are loosed into the atmosphere. Sometimes – in dry conditions – they evaporate immediately, and sometimes they persist and spread across the sky, seeding ambient moisture already present to form vast, horizon-filling cirriform structures that began life in an aeroplane's fuel tank. These are what the theorists call chemtrails. What I didn't mention in the book, mostly because of a restricted word count, is that the idea of a vast, global conspiracy involving thousands of individuals and dozens of government agencies around the world, ranging from NASA to the Civil Aviation Authority, being able to secretly poison the entire human population (including, presumably, the perpetrators themselves) over many years, without a single data breach or whistle-blower coming forward, is the most preposterous thing I've ever heard. Do these people not know how incompetent and leak-prone all government bodies are? How most attempts at cross-border collaboration collapse amid mutual recriminations? The unprecedented scale and apparent success of the global chemtrail conspiracy are the very things that prove it can't be true.

But the more you deny the truth of something, the more it looks like part of the conspiracy. "Of course these claims have been refuted by the military as well as by federal agencies such as NASA," I wrote, "which leaves the conspiracy theorists even more convinced of the existence of a high-level cover-up."[2] It was only one line in an otherwise even-toned book, and though I was secretly quite pleased with that mildly snarky "high-level cover-up", I had no idea how much trouble those words were going to cause me. For, as I soon discovered, there are plenty of chemtrail activists out there, busily (and angrily) blogging and tweeting and messaging their days away, and it wasn't long before they had organised a coordinated one-star Amazon review campaign, targeting my series of Met Office books: "Richard Hamblyn is a paid liar"; "When will the Met Office start telling the truth?"; "Don't believe their vile lies"; "Who is going to stop them? Chemtrails are real".

Not long after, a series of insinuating emails began to arrive in my work inbox, one every few days, sent from a variety of pseudonymous accounts:

> Hey Richard, looks like your [sic] making a good living from your lies. How much are they paying you?
>
> When are you going to start telling the truth?
>
> Why are you covering up for them? How much are they paying you?
>
> "Doctor", take pity on humanity and stop your lies
>
> "Doctor", a word of advice. It will be better for you if you stop lying

It was that last one that made my mouth go dry. Was I being threatened? It was hard to tell, though the more I read and reread the message, parsing every opaque nuance, the more disturbing it appeared. I was working in central London at the time, at the UCL Environment Institute, and anyone could have walked past reception and made their way to my office. The thought that there were people out there angry enough to send hostile emails and post defamatory reviews was extremely unsettling. It was also oddly aggravating to be accused of being well paid to cover up the truth, for at the time I had never felt poorer. I thought of posting one of the royalty cheques that I receive every year from the Met Office (I once got one for seventy-three pence), but decided against it on the grounds of embarrassment. I also thought how welcome it would be to be offered a fortune for suppressing the truth, but the sad fact is that I was, and remain, a minor-league academic and author who wouldn't be worth the trouble of corrupting.

But, of course, as a non-fiction writer, the imputation of deceit is uniquely damaging, and I needed to do something about those reviews. The Amazon helpdesk proved woefully misnamed, since they refused to act when I first approached them, claiming that nothing in the reviews breached their "community guidelines". "But they're calling me a liar," I said, "a paid liar," yet apparently this wasn't enough. When I mentioned the Met Office legal department, however, the reviews were taken down within an hour. The emails stopped coming after a couple of weeks, nobody stalked me in my Gower Street lair, and after a while I began to assume that my first encounter with the chemtrail people would also be my last.

You already know how the next line goes.

How wrong I was.

Climate change is a serious subject, so why do I keep wanting to laugh? Why was it funny when they stuck a couple of recycling bins next to a billion tonnes of freshly poured concrete and called it "the greenest Olympics ever"? Why do I snigger every time I remember a conference where no one could agree on how to pronounce the surname of William Whewell, the Victorian polymath who coined the word "scientist" in 1834? That week had heard a wealth of discussion about our atmospheric future, but all I remember is the whistling birdsong made by a hallful of earnest delegates attempting to get their mouths around Whewell's unpronounceable name. Most academic conferences are absurd, but climate change conferences are in a league of their own. A few years ago, during one of the annual UN climate change jamborees that fail to save the world, that fail even to agree that the world needs saving, a cartoon of genius appeared in, I think, *The New Yorker*. The setting was one of the conference halls visited by the UN's itinerant talking shop – maybe it was COP15, in Copenhagen's gleaming Bella Center, or perhaps it was the following year's beanfeast in Cancún, Mexico; anyway, the cartoon showed a member of the audience addressing the

"...√hat if climate change turns out to be a hoax," he was
"...'and we end up creating a cleaner, more equitable planet
thing?"

...chink about that cartoon a lot. In fact I was thinking about
...ٍ I walked up Exhibition Road on a warm September morning
in 2015, on my way to give a talk at the inaugural London
Conference of the Cloud Appreciation Society, an informal
association of self-styled "cloud geeks" that had been started as
a short-lived joke some ten years before, but which had grown
into a slickly run online club with more than forty thousand
paid-up members. I had prepared a thirty-minute talk – it was
going to be about the language of clouds – but I was wondering
whether to start with the climate change cartoon, and how the
punchline might go down in the room: "What if we end up saving
the world *for nothing*?" Would they laugh, or would they think I
was trying too hard? Of course you never know what you're
going to encounter when it comes to giving a talk: bafflement,
hostility, a malfunctioning projector. But as I drew nearer to the
conference venue – the venerable Royal Geographical Society – I
was surprised to find that it was being noisily picketed by a
thirty- or forty-strong group of protesters, complete with placards
and handbills. Chemtrail activists. "Your all liars," read one of
the placards, and I wondered, with a small stab of recognition,
whether it had been written by the same ungrammatical hand
that had sent the "looks like your making a good living from
your lies" message a few years before. "Your" for "you're" is a
common enough mistake, as I discover every year during marking
season, but there was something about the particular phrasing
that put me on high alert.

I had, in fact, started receiving chemtrail-related emails again,
though they were not as sinister as before, being framed, for the
most part, as polite enquiries, which I answered with a standard
response. Those who replied to my answers tended to become
less polite as the exchanges went on, and I had recently taken to
deleting and blocking all messages on the subject without reading
them. What irritated me more than the chemtrail obsession was
the fact that the conspirators are also enthusiastic climate change
deniers, for whom the "myth" of atmospheric warming is just

another example of high-level collusion designed to place secretive, tax-drunk governments in charge of every aspect of our lives (I am paraphrasing).

What they've enacted is a curious alt-right inversion of environmentalism that dismisses human-made climate change, while fixating on the idea of a secret programme of state-level weather control, as outlined in a multi-coloured leaflet that was thrust into my hand as I reached the door of the conference venue. "Geo-engineering (cloud seeding, chemtrails, sky dimming, solar radiation management, ocean fertilization, Stratospheric Aerosol Geo-Engineering) is responsible for Weather Manipulation, Sky Darkening, Deforestation, Air Pollution, Soil Contamination," it read, followed by a long list of negative health effects that concluded with, ironically, "paranoia".

I mumbled a thank-you, keeping my head down.

"You going to this *scum* conference, then?" the leaflet man demanded. "With all the *liars*?"

I wish I could say that this was when I made my witty and devastating reply, that I looked the leaflet man in the eye and told him, calmly and irrefutably, that anyone can see that human activity has written its visible signature on the skies, and that horizon-filling displays of dissipated contrails are now among the most common cloud formations in the world; that humanity is indeed pumping deadly chemicals into the atmosphere, in the form of carbon dioxide and water vapour, two of the most potent and damaging greenhouse emissions, and that if we don't do something about it, and soon, we'll be suffering from more than paranoia. But the truth is, my heart was hammering and my throat was closing up with anxiety, as I found myself face to face on a Kensington pavement with a middle-aged man who, I strongly suspected, had been responsible for sending me abusive emails and for trolling me online, or at the very least had travelled into London for the day with someone who had. All the considered views on the chemtrail conspiracy that I had formulated over the years – that it depends on a chimerically elaborate degree of inter-governmental collusion; that it obsesses over a fictitious threat while dismissing a real and immediate one; that it attracts a similar brand of anti-science contrarian as the newly resurgent

Flat Earth Society – deserted me entirely, as I thought how *unfair* it was. After all, what could be more harmless, more foolishly English, than a cloud appreciation society, yet here we were being picketed and accused as though we were arms dealers, as though we were an oil company that had just started drilling on Antarctica. As a chant began to spread among the protestors – "*Liars, liars, liars, liars!*" – I found myself frozen to the spot.

Most writers will find themselves experiencing feelings they had not anticipated, either in terms of the content of their projects, or their relationship to the writing process itself, with all its complicated pleasures and pains. Within the academy there are no guidelines on how to manage unexpected emotions that might undermine or overwhelm one's research, whether they are feelings of anger, guilt, shame, disgust, offence, frustration, boredom, anxiety, fear. We will all experience such states during our writing lives – it would be strange if we didn't – but any one of them can turn up one day and pitch us sideways with surprise. A seminar held in my department last year, entitled "Researching (With) Difficult Feelings", set out to address this issue head-on, and in the light of several years of encounters with chemtrail activists, online and in person, I found myself reflecting for the first time on what I felt as well as what I thought about them. I'm fortunate in my critical moment: after Sianne Ngai's landmark book *Ugly Feelings*, there has been a wealth of scholarship in this area, and the history of emotions has developed into a particularly rich and provocative area of research.[3]

Thinking about it, I wondered whether "wariness" counts as an emotion, for that had become my default setting in the wake of the Amazon reviews. I had tried to avoid any engagement with the chemtrail narrative, and have never referred to it in print again, until now. I wondered about the wisdom of discussing it here, and while I would never put the word "chemtrails" in a title, I decided that it was time to try to write my way out of my wariness. Also, a small body of scholarship on the subject has recently emerged, mostly from a social science perspective, to which I find myself cautiously drawn. An article by Greek anthropologist Alexandra Bakalaki, entitled "Chemtrails, Crisis, and Loss in an Interconnected World", appeared in 2016, in which Bakalaki described how chemtrail narratives became prevalent in Greece after the economic crash of 2009.[4] They offered a means of challenging official narratives, she wrote, not only about climate and global risk, but more directly about the handling of the Greek economy. Bakalaki unearthed claims of atmospheric spraying by "US Zionist and Masonic circles who want to undermine Greece's political autonomy", in which weather manipulation was identified as a growing political and economic threat across Europe.

It was a fascinating read, and led me to an earlier article, "Climates of Suspicion", which had appeared in *The Geographical Journal* in 2014. The paper, by Rose Cairns, from the University of Sussex Science Policy Research Unit, argued that to dismiss such discourses as merely pathological was to overlook revealing insights into the wider cultural politics of our atmosphere. Cairns took an avowedly Foucauldian approach to chemtrail narratives, reading them as a form of outsider science, "knowledge-producing discourses" that challenge the dominant narratives produced by mainstream science.[5] The chemtrail conspiracy is unusual because it is not a self-contained counter-narrative such as the "hoax moon landing" hypothesis; instead it aligns closely with well-established, legitimate anxieties about our planet's contaminated skies. The crossover between conspiracy narrative and mainstream critique can be disarmingly close. As the philosopher Bruno Latour pointed out in his influential essay "Why Has Critique Run Out of Steam?" (2004), social theorists and conspiracy theorists often share arguments in common; "Of course," he notes, "we in the academy like to use more elevated causes – society, discourse, knowledge-slash-power, fields of forces, empires, capitalism – while conspiracists like to portray a miserable bunch of greedy people with dark intents, but I find something troublingly similar in the structure of the explanation".[6]

Well, yes, but while I have an instinctive sympathy for Cairns's approach, and agree that we should acknowledge the legitimacy of voices that challenge the dominant discourse, this is where personal feelings complicate the equation. The problem I have with seeing chemtrail activists as quasi-heroic Foucauldian outsiders whose anti-corporate counter-narratives speak truth to power, is that the vision falls down when you discover that they are, for the most part, misogynist Trump supporters who spend their lives online, dishing out slander to anyone they disagree with, including to Rose Cairns herself after her paper was published. A lengthy article, entitled "Rose Cairns, Sussex U. Grant-Funded Chemtrail Debunker, Makes a Living Proffering Government/Establishment Denial Propaganda Dressed Up as Peer Reviewed 'Science'", appeared on the *Educate-Yourself* website (a New World Order conspiracy forum) in which a series of personal attacks on Cairns made for disquieting reading. Aside from the predictable misogyny and contempt, the article was notable for misunderstanding Cairns's argument, which was no debunking exercise, but a nuanced and sympathetic discussion of the chemtrailers' position – certainly far more nuanced and sympathetic than I would ever have been.[7]

As Cairns rightly cautioned, it's a mistake to situate such narratives along traditional left/right political axes, since for chemtrail activists, as for most other conspiracy theorists, the overriding belief is that nothing happens by accident. So it is easy to see why they would reject the argument that collectively, albeit unintentionally, humanity is altering Earth's climate in catastrophic ways. If nothing happens unintentionally, including planetary processes, then the association between chemtrail conspiracy and climate change denial makes perfect, swivel-eyed, Borgesian sense.

The trouble with climate change is that it's too big to see. It's one of those entities that the ecocritic Timothy Morton called a "hyperobject", hyperobjectivity being one of those ideas that became so rapidly and annoyingly ubiquitous it was easy to forget how brilliant it was.[8] Hyperobjects are things – either physical or conceptual – that are too big to see, but that are always there, impacting on our lives whether or not we give them any thought. In some ways climate change is the greatest hyperobject of them all, being too big to see, too big to imagine, too big to compare to anything else. Its bigness is what makes the activist Greta Thunberg's smallness so powerful, as hinted at in the title of her published speeches, *No One is Too Small to Make a Difference*, in which she invokes the seriousness of our climate crisis in stark, elliptical statements:

> I don't want you to be hopeful.
>
> I want you to panic.
>
> I want you to feel the fear I feel every day.
>
> And then I want you to act.
>
> I want you to act as you would in a crisis.
>
> I want you to act as if our house is on fire.
>
> Because it is.[9]

She's right, of course, but she's picked an unwinnable fight against an invisible foe.

If the sky somehow changed colour as a result of increased greenhouse emissions, there wouldn't be a problem now: catastrophe would have been averted long ago. But since our skies look more or less the same no matter what we pump into them, what is needed is some kind of convincing visual representation – a clinching metaphor for atmospheric change – such as the brilliantly coloured graphics that showed the ever-widening "hole" in the ozone layer above Antarctica. First published by NASA in the 1980s, those luminous green/blue graphics succeeded in visualising an otherwise invisible process so strikingly that the world was alerted in time to a looming environmental threat.

The process was remarkably quick. In the 1970s, researchers at the British Antarctic Survey discovered that ozone concentrations above Antarctica were depleting fast, and that the level of ultraviolet radiation reaching the poles was increasing as a result. The culprit was soon identified: chlorofluorocarbons (CFCs), human-made compounds invented by industrial chemists in the late 1920s, and put to use in a range of applications, including refrigerators, air conditioners, solvents and propellants. By 1975, spray cans alone were pumping half a billion tonnes of them into the atmosphere, and ten years later, worldwide production of CFCs stood at almost two billion tonnes per year. The problem with these compounds is that once they have evaporated into the stratosphere, they are broken down by ultraviolet radiation, and their chlorine atoms released. Since chlorine can remain aloft for many decades, during which time a single atom can catalytically convert up to one hundred thousand ozone molecules into oxygen, even over the Earth's mid-latitudes, it soon became apparent that the "ozone hole" over Antarctica was only the opening rend in our planet's protecting veil.

The wake-up call came in the form of a paper published in the journal *Nature* in May 1985, in which the severity of the threat was demonstrated beyond doubt.[10] NASA's visualisations were widely reproduced, and the combination of instrumental evidence and compelling graphic imagery galvanised the world into action. The United States took the lead by banning the use of CFCs in spray cans, and a couple of years later, the United Nations Environment Programme proposed the creation of a global convention guaranteeing the protection of the ozone layer. In 1987, this UN convention led to the signing of the Montreal Protocol, a treaty that deserves to be better known than it is, since it represents humanity's first victory over a global environmental crisis. Compared with the embarrassing political quagmire that was the Kyoto Protocol negotiations, or the more recent "promises" enshrined in the 2016 Paris Agreement, the Montreal treaty was a model of effective international action, with every developed nation in the world committing itself to the elimination of CFCs from all industrial processes by 1996. Nearly a quarter of a century on from that first Montreal deadline, and the ozone hole can be seen to be healing. It's a slow process, due mostly to the longevity of ozone-eating chlorine, but at current rates, ozone concentrations over the poles will have been restored to their pre-industrial levels by the middle of the present century.

Of course, it was relatively easy to remove chlorofluorocarbons from the global economy. They may have been hugely damaging, but they were also a niche product. Emancipating ourselves from fossil fuels, on which every form of human activity now depends, is of a different order of magnitude, requiring nothing short of a conceptual leap into the unknown. For we don't just need to find an "ozone hole" equivalent for the bigger crisis of climate change, although our gallery of alarmist icons is looking pretty jaded these days (melting glaciers, stranded polar bears, dried-out riverbeds, drowned coastlines). No, forget the tired visuals: the task now is emotional, because what we need to discover and develop – perhaps for the first time in human history – is a profound collective empathy for the future.

So there I was, on the pavement outside the Royal Geographical Society, having failed to answer the question of whether or not I was going to this *"scum* conference", while the *"liars"* chant began to fade away. I had so many things to say – all the things I have now said in this essay – but my throat was still tight and my blood was echoing noisily in my head, and I found I couldn't utter a word.

It was the intensity of their anger that made the protestors so alarming, the fervour of their mistaken belief in conspiracy rather than crisis. What would be gained by telling this man that he was angry with all the wrong people? What would be gained by telling him anything at all? Still holding the flyer, I turned and hurried into the blockaded building, past the security desk and into the lanyard-and-welcome-packed safety of the conference hall, where a hundred delegates from around the world were gathering, once again, to talk about the weather.

1 James Inhofe, *The Greatest Hoax: How the Global Warming Conspiracy Threatens Your Future* (Washington, DC: WND Books, 2012), 3.
2 Richard Hamblyn, *Extraordinary Clouds: Skies of the Unexpected from the Beautiful to the Bizarre* (Newton Abbot: David & Charles, 2009), 49.
3 Sianne Ngai, *Ugly Feelings* (Cambridge, MA: Harvard University Press, 2005).
4 Alexandra Bakalaki, "Chemtrails, Crisis, and Loss in an Interconnected World", *Visual Anthropology Review*, 32/1 (2016), 12–23.
5 Rose Cairns, "Climates of Suspicion: 'Chemtrail' Conspiracy Narratives and the International Politics of Geoengineering", *The Geographical Journal*, 182/1 (2014), 70–84.

6   Bruno Latour, "Why Has Critique Run Out of Steam? From Matters of Fact to Matters of Concern", *Critical Inquiry*, 30 (Winter 2004), 229.

7   Educate-Yourself, "Rose Cairns, Sussex U. Grant-Funded Chemtrail Debunker, Makes a Living Proffering Government/Establishment Denial Propaganda Dressed Up as Peer Reviewed 'Science'" (5 July 2015). http://educate-yourself.org/cn/Rose-Cairns-Sussex-U-Grant-Funded-Chemtrail-Debunker05jul15.shtml> accessed 10 June 2019.
     I'm very aware that the negative attention I receive would be far more personal and threatening if I weren't male, if I weren't white. In my case, most of the slander is to do with money, accusing me of profiting from my lies, of being too well-paid to ever give them up. As mentioned above, accusations of being a paid shill are irritating rather than frightening, "irritation" being one of Sianne Ngai's case-study "ugly feelings" in her book. Irritation is ugly, she argues, because it's non-cathartic; it's a feeling that you can't do anything positive with, for unlike fear or righteous anger it just sits there nibbling at you until it goes away.

8   See Timothy Morton, *Hyperobjects: Philosophy and Ecology after the End of the World* (Minneapolis: University of Minnesota Press, 2013).

9   Greta Thunberg, *No One is Too Small to Make a Difference* (London: Penguin, 2019), 24.

10   J. C. Farman, B. G. Gardiner & J. D. Shanklin, "Large losses of total ozone in Antarctica reveal seasonal ClO_x/NO_x interaction", *Nature*, 315 (16 May 1985), 207–210.

FICTION

SPECKS

EMMA HUTTON

T he day the doctor tells you and your husband to stop trying for a baby, a dead whale washes up on the beach. At home, you switch the television on and watch as the newsreader says there are no trucks big enough to haul the whale away. Men in neoprene suits crowd the blue-black body; the glint of a blade bigger than you can imagine moves back and forth across its middle. You cry as your husband puts his hand on the back of your neck. You see the blade disappear into the shiny black, until it meets the meat of it and everything is suddenly red. Out pour things you did not expect: flip-flops, water bottles, a white plastic garden chair, those flimsy blue bags you carry bottles of Merlot home in from the corner shop.

Your husband thinks you are crying about the baby you can't make with your body but really you are crying about the whale, gashed open, split apart, full of endings. Your husband doesn't know that you don't care about the baby, that you only care about your plan. And the baby you can't have is ruining that plan.

It began when they pulled you out of the red mess of your mother's middle. She started to plot points on the imaginary map of your life – the right things in the right order: university, a job, a decent man to turn into a husband, a baby. You followed the plan, stuck to it even when she died two days after your twenty-third birthday. It was all you knew, all you wanted to know. Passed down from mother to mother to mother. You did not consider deviating from the plan, did not think that was possible. There was only A, then B, then C. To depart from alphabetic inevitability was to be somewhere you were un-prepared for. Unbidden. So earlier that morning, when the doctor said the words "inhospitable uterus", you laughed. The plan has taught you that those two words do not belong together. You pictured your womb as an unfriendly hostess, some sort of terrible Mrs Dalloway.

"Inhospitable," you said, and laughed again. Then came your mother's voice, ringing out over the loudspeaker of your hippocampus: *Stay the course*, it commanded, but you were in the unknown – mapless, motherless and as good as alone.

The doctor said it would be wise to consider adoption. Another word you were unprepared for. Your husband shook his head and you listened as the plastic chair cracked and bent beneath him.

You first met him at a gallery in the city. He was so tall his body couldn't keep up with him. Parts dragged behind as though they were caught in another frame. A leg. An arm. When he hauled himself into focus you could see that there was just too much of him. He wore a heavy blue coat, a little short in the sleeves. You could tell it was expensive by the colour, a blue you did not see often.

You sat on a bench in the middle of a room filled with gold-framed paintings. He reached out to touch the green of a stocking, half fallen down the leg of a half-naked girl. You remember the lurid pink of her nipples, how you thought nipples could never be that colour in real life. As you sat there, the static-furred noise of your mother's voice shot through you.

A man with money.

Tall men make good babies.

Do whatever it takes to get him.

His fingers extended, but before they hit the canvas a woman in black cleared her throat and he turned towards her. They smiled at each other. The symmetry of his face made you forget time for a moment.

Of course he wanted to reach out. It was the reaching out that made you want him, that made you think he was the "right" one. Made you want to bite the skin of his wrist hard enough to leave a curve of teeth marks for days.

You followed him out of the exhibition and into the café, where you choreographed a fall Gene Kelly would have been proud of. He picked you up, obviously, because that was part of the plan. He sat you in a booth in the corner and helped you take off your coat. He brought you tea in a pot which he poured from a height. Drips fell onto the white of the table. You talked and talked, and he told you he had always dreamt of being an artist but he was not, he was a man who wore a suit and worked in the City. When he asked what it was you did, you inhaled and whispered, "Lepidopterist." You were so accustomed to the inevitable follow-up questions that it drained you.

"They still exist?"

"They do." You smiled.

Later, after the café and a trip to the rooftop bar for too many glasses of champagne, you went home with him and shivered as he put his hand on the base of your spine and gently pressed as though there was a button and he was switching you on.

It was easy after that. You went for more drinks and ate dinners. You watched black-and-white films filled with tall men and perfect women. Made extravagant meals and threw away the leftovers. Walked through parks and stayed in hotels. No spells were cast or rituals performed; you did what you had to do to secure him, what your mother told you to do: you made yourself fit him. You bent, retracted, swooned, sucked in air and blew it out again. You made shapes. You made him love you. You married at thirty-one, left the city, bought a house by the sea. Then you tried for a baby until the doctor said "inhospitable" and your husband shook his head.

Not long after this, the sand comes.

At first, you feel it on the soles of your feet. Dirt from shoes, you think, as you hoover the house on Saturday – cleaning day. The next morning, as you walk from the bedroom to the bathroom, tiny grains cluster beneath your feet and get caught between your toes. You sit on the toilet seat, brushing them away with the palm of your hand, watching as they fall to the floor. Sandstorms in the Sahara bring red skies. You look out the bathroom window. The sky is grey.

Over the next few days, sand piles up in corners and on sills. You clean when it is not cleaning day. You convince yourself it's something to do with the weather so you shut all the windows, but nothing changes. The sand is still there.

In bed, you ask your husband if he can feel it.

"Feel what?" he says.

"The sand. It's everywhere. Haven't you seen it?"

"It's probably just fallen off my trainers."

"But you don't run along the beach."

"Go to sleep." He sighs.

Weeks pass but the sand is still there. You shake it out of shoes lined up beside the kitchen door. You send your husband pictures of the mounds forming on the window sills but he tells you there is nothing there. He says maybe you should "see someone".

You notice that on your daily morning walks to the sea he no longer guides you to the inside of the pavement. You tell him you think the beach is getting smaller, receding as hotels and empty apartment blocks rise up in front of the shoreline.

He shrugs.

As fresh bodies dive off the harbour wall you can tell he is thinking about your inhospitable womb.

You spend afternoons watching documentaries about the ice caps melting, about wildfires and droughts. Voiceovers inform you that the sand is running out, that it is being dredged to make cement. "Sand is a finite resource," the voice says. *Finite.* You repeat the word over and over in your head until it stops making sense.

One evening, your husband takes you to the restaurant on the beach for dinner. He orders oysters and the second most expensive bottle of wine.

"Shellfish are dissolving in the oceans," you say as he lifts an oyster to his mouth. "Did you know that?"

"I didn't. Did you see that on one of your documentaries?"

You nod and eat the hake he ordered for you.

"Why are they dissolving?"

"It's the acid in the ocean. It makes their shells soft. It's *our* fault," you say, gesturing to all the bodies sitting in chairs, clanking their knives and forks.

"That sounds a little extreme. What about your precious butterflies?" He laughs. "Are they dissolving too?"

"Not dissolving, more like disappearing."

"Because you chased them away with your little net?" He laughs again. "So what can we do to stop all the dissolving and disappearing?"

"It's too late to do anything now."

"Cheer up. It's not the end of the world."

"What if it is?" you say, pushing yourself up from the table. You feel him rolling his eyes as you walk to the bathroom.

In the days after dinner at the restaurant you think only of your wayward body. Your husband stops grabbing your hair when you fuck. He spends most evenings at the gym. His shirts start to split across the shoulders. You stop making the bed and your husband sleeps in the guest room. You stop going to the university where you work. You stop making dinner and only eat watermelons, peaches and peanuts; you have lost the taste for other things. When you forget to buy your mother-in-law a birthday present, your husband tells you it's time to see the doctor.

"This can't go on," he says.

You feel your bones go soft.

"How do you feel?" the doctor asks. He's wearing a Santa hat and chewing the end of a yellow pencil, the pink rubber already gone.

"Nice hat," you say.

"The kids like it. You look tired. Are you sleeping?"

"I can't sleep. The sand gets into everything. Will you look in my ears? I can feel it in my ears."

He reaches down for the bottom drawer of his desk and pulls an otoscope out of its little black case before slipping across the linoleum floor to stick it in your ear.

"Nothing there, I'm afraid." He shakes his head. "No sand. *Nada.*"

"Am I imagining it all?" you say, thinking this is the moment when he tells you that you are crazy.

"I had a woman who used to come in here saying her house was filling up with water. Icy-cold blue-black water from the Arctic she said." He smiles, sitting back down and chewing on the yellow pencil. "She said she was going to drown."

"What happened to her?"

"No idea. Eaten by a polar bear?" He laughs. "Don't worry." He reaches out and puts his hand on your knee. "She just had a touch of the baby blues."

"Look," you say, lifting your phone to show him photographs of the sand. He shakes his head.

"I see from your file that you've had some problems conceiving. Do you think that might have something to do with how you're feeling? What you're … seeing?"

"Maybe," you lie, knowing it's not about the baby, it's about the plan that got messed up because of your broken body and now everything is off course.

"You're run-down. You need to get some rest. Why don't you try meditation? And stop thinking so much."

Thinking too much only leads to trouble. The crackle of your mother's voice works its way through every cell of your body.

The doctor starts punching the keys of his computer, and you picture the monkey from a GIF someone sent you once. Eventually the printer kicks into action and cranks out a small square of paper. "Here," he says, handing you a prescription filled with row after row of words with too many syllables.

"What's this?"

"The good stuff," he says, standing up and skating across the floor to open the door for you. "Call me if you need to," he says, "and don't blame yourself. It's not your fault your body's a dud. Merry Christmas!"

On the bus home you lean your head against the window and make yourself as small as possible. You wonder how long it will take your husband to leave you and try to think of reasons for him to stay but come up short. You think about the woman with water filling up her house. You search the Internet but can't find anything about her, at least not when you type: "woman house filled with Arctic water". You type: "woman eaten by polar bear" but stop yourself from hitting the blue Go button. Instead, you close your eyes and imagine a grey polar bear sitting on a velvet sofa in the living room of a semi-detached house. Behind you a little girl turns to her mother. "What does the sun smell like?" You open your eyes.

You stop at the chemist and pick up bottles of pills with names you can't pronounce. At home, you tip them into your cupped palm. The instructions say to swallow with water but you crunch them between your teeth.

You take the tablets for a week but the sand is still there. You can't sleep and one night you sit cross-legged on the living-room floor and watch a meditation video. You copy the woman in the video and recite the mantra over and over until it turns into *dud, dud, dud.* In the morning, your husband finds you face down on the carpet. He steps over your body and out the front door.

You call the doctor.

"I need to know what's wrong with me," you say into the phone. "Can you tell me? Can you give it a name?"

"Have you been taking your tablets like a good girl?"

"Yes" – you swallow – "but when will they start working?"

"Different strokes for different folks," he says, chewing on something. "Look, it doesn't matter what we call it. It is what it is."

It is what it is. Your mother's favourite refrain whirs in the spaces between your bones.

"Why don't you go online and buy yourself something nice in the sales. That'll make you feel better."

"My computer is full of sand."

"Did I ever tell you about the woman who thought her house was on fire?" He laughs and you recall the glint of a blade and the whale's split middle. "She said her bed was burning, thought the fire would get her in her sleep. She cried and cried but what could I do?"

"What did you do?"

"I told her to get some rest, just like you."

On New Year's Eve you have a dinner party for your husband's family because you always have a dinner party for his family on New Year's Eve. Up before him, you brush as much sand as you can out the kitchen door and into the back garden. You will tell him you are feeling better. It is grasping at straws but you do not know what else to do. You make him breakfast and take it to the guest room, setting the tray on his lap and pouring the coffee. "The sand is gone," you say. "The pills must be working."

"Really?" he asks, biting into a sausage.

"Yes," you say, opening the curtains to find a skinny fox diving into the sand piled up in the garden, rolling around on its back.

That night your sister-in-law sits beside you on the sofa. "Are you OK?" she asks, the silver sequins of her dress scratching your arm.

The sand is back, covering everything. You flick a pile of grains from your shoulder and ask her, "Is your house full of sand too?" She shakes her head, pats your knee and stands. You look on as she selects a bottle of gin from the drinks tray on the table and dusts off the cap. She pours until it hits the rim of the champagne flute, lifts the glass to her mouth and tips it up by the stem. Her throat retracts and releases as the liquid slips down. It reminds you of the lizard you kept in a glass box as a child. You fed it hard-bodied insects that it cracked apart in its mouth before swallowing them down, half dead, half alive. She looks at you, pours another and smiles.

At the dinner table, you spoon Parmesan from an overflowing bowl; half sand. You tell yourself you are imagining it as his family wind strings of spaghetti around forks and plunge them into their mouths. You do the same but it won't stay down. You cough the spaghetti back onto your plate and keep coughing until hands come to rest on your back.

"It's OK. You're OK," your mother-in-law whispers in your ear.

"It's the sand," you spit out, the words forming a claggy mess in your mouth.

"There's no sand," your husband's family chorus, but you can see it between their teeth, in the corners of their mouths. You laugh.

"She's tired," your husband explains, dragging you from the table and up the stairs to your bedroom where he sits you on the bed. "You need to cut this out. You sound crazy."

"But it's in your mouth!"

"What is? Sand? There's no sand. It's all in your head." He points a finger to his own head. "All. In. Your. Head."

"Please." You reach out to him, crying. "I need you to see it too."

"It's time to plan what's going to happen next. The doctor said there are options to consider. Places you can go for treatment."

"Plan?" You didn't know about this plan. Another plan you did not make. "You spoke to the doctor? My doctor?"

"We'll talk in the morning," he says, as the fireworks start, walking out and kicking over a tiny dune as he goes.

At the window you look for Venus because your mother told you it was the brightest planet in the sky. Your mother thought

Venus must be the most beautiful of all the planets because it was the brightest, but she didn't know about its inhospitable landscape made of volcanoes and deformed mountains, the endless acid rain. You find it easily, dangling by the moon, and will your body to be transported to its surface. When that fails, you imagine the damage a fall from a second-storey window would cause. Not enough, you think, as two taxis pull up outside your front door. You lean your hip against the glass and watch as his family say their goodbyes and step out onto the pavement.

I *am* a terrible hostess, you think, and wonder what they are saying about you. They are probably calling you crazy, saying they are glad he is finally going to put you away. You go to close the curtain but stop when your sister-in-law opens her huge fake-leather bag. She pulls out plastic water bottle after plastic water bottle and hands them around. They tilt them to their lips, swilling the water before spitting it onto the road. You feel the carefully drawn lines of yourself warp and shift. You watch as your mother-in-law takes off her black shoes and turns over each one, spilling sand onto the wet tarmac. She looks up at the window. You make a fist but don't strike the glass. Instead, you raise your wrist to your mouth, biting hard enough to leave half-moons of teeth you will find in the morning.

You sleep for seven hours, the longest you have slept since you found out about your inhospitable body. You shake the sand off the bedcovers, run your feet over the beach of a carpet. In the bathroom you find your husband rubbing his eyes. He looks at your naked body reflected in the mirror. "Soap," he says, his eyes streaming red from the sand fallen into them overnight.

"Liar," you say, grabbing your robe from its hook and pulling the door closed before the hand he has reached out can touch you.

You want to leave, to be anywhere your husband is not, but the sand has climbed the stairs and there is no way down. You turn back to the bedroom and call the doctor.

"Happy New Year," he says.

"I'm not crazy."

"Nobody said you were."

"They can see it."

"I know I said to call me any time, but this is a bit much."

"They can see the sand. It's real." You look down at the toothy crescents on your wrist.

"Why don't you pop into the surgery and see me the day after tomorrow," he says. "We can talk about the sand then. And the next steps."

"No. You should come and see the sand for yourself."

"That's not how it's done," he says. "Why don't you go and lie down, get some rest."

No rest for the wicked, your mother coos in your ear.

"What happened to them? The other women you told to get some rest. Where are they now?"

"I'm going to call your husband," he says.

"Tell me what happened to them."

"You're really doing yourself no favours with this behaviour."

You walk to the window and push it open, launch the phone into the sky. You don't see where it falls. You look out over the rows of houses that surround you and imagine the people inside them. The women. Making breakfast, folding sheets, wiping the shit off toilet bowls. You imagine the plans and plotted constellations of their lives, maps that were made for them.

You look and look and not too far away you see smoke rising from a window. You see fire behind glass. You look again and see more windows with more fires. One, two, three, four ... You lose count when you spot a house with every window cracked and watch as blue-black water pours out onto the street below. You find another house with broken windows, and another. Behind one you see a speck, and wave.

Please see me, you think.

You wave and wave and soon the speck waves back. And then another speck in another window. And another. You see them all at once, the specks. The women. The women swimming upstairs through ice-cold Arctic water to wave at you. The women dancing through houses full of fire to reach their hands out to you. The women climbing over dunes to get to you.

You laugh, crunching the sand between your teeth.

You can see me, you think. You can see me.

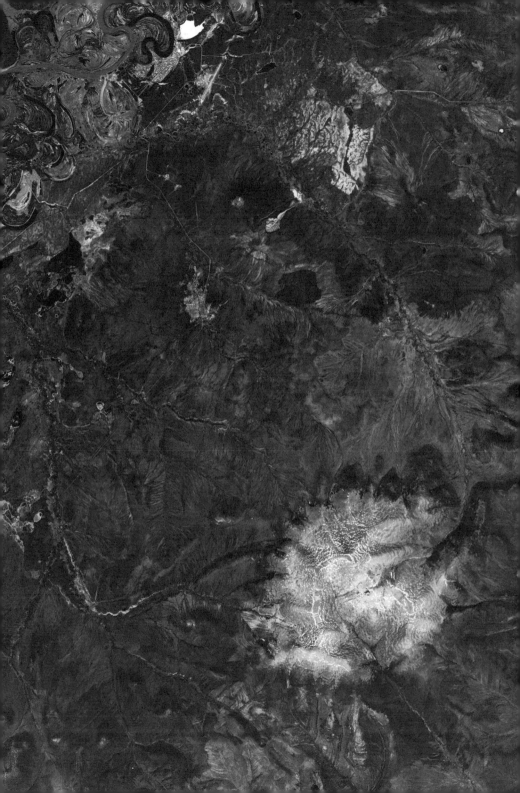

POETRY

HAIBUN MELTDOWN

SLUMP

FLOOD

DROUGHT

SMOG

RACHEL BOWER

HAIBUN MELTDOWN

Svalbard Archipelago, Norway

Picture the game where you rip a sheet of newspaper in half every time the music stops. The children crowd unnaturally close on tiny pieces of print. Soon they will start to fall off. I catch one, collect his tears, but do not know where to tip them. I decide to freeze them in little blocks for later. The party is ruined, children flapping everywhere.

dazzling blue ice caps
cracked to polystyrene bits
floating in blackness

SLUMP

Batagaika Crater, Northern Yakutia, Eastern Siberia

Drunken spruces stagger around the edge,
buckling, sinking with the thaw. The crater

swallows more of the hillside each year,
disturbing mammoths and elks. One landslide

wakes an ancient foal, another a bison calf.
They slip unsteadily into the deserted village

of thermokarst tents. Scientists flock to date
the layers, but locals stay away from this opening

to the underworld, with rightful dread.
It is the modern-day bottomless pit, even the devils

freed from the permafrost, crouched, sweating
in the dust, calling, calling to us all:

Come, bring your gold, your myrrh, your hearts.
Come, join us in this seething chasm of dirt.

The excitement mounts, the crowd surges forward.
This is no abyss between the righteous

dead and the wicked dead, but a dreadful siren
wailing, dragging us down with the crumbling rock.

FLOOD

Jamalpur District, Bangladesh

The woman stands at the front
of the raft looking straight

ahead. She bends from the waist,
presses down with a bamboo stick.

The water reflects the marigolds
on her green silk sari.

Her feet are bare, tired.
She does not think of grilled corn

or sugar and rice pounded to *lai*.
Lime trees wait on the horizon

casually kicking brown water.
This is not a lake so there is no shore.

DROUGHT

Purulia District, West Bengal

The sky is a bruise, the earth a cracked foot.
An army of tiny pylons march on the horizon
like ants, carrying the spoils of the day
high above their heads. An occasional wasp grub
crackles, but there is no chance of escape.

The sky is an oven, the earth a split crust.
In the distance, a bicycle bumps over bedrock,
flour billowing around its tyres.
There is no *ghee* to puff the dough
so it brings dust instead. The land thirsts for *mishti doi.*

The sky is a shriek, the earth a fractured bowl.
The potter throws dirt from his wheel,
thumbs caked with *patali gur*, thickly baked
to gloves. His fingertips are numb
as he rubs burnt curd into his feet.

SMOG

Hebei Province, China

> No blue sky this year,
> only a sour yellow taste
> in the heart and throat.

*

There is a photo. A woman and boy play ping-pong outdoors. The game is utterly silent. The tap of the ball is smothered. The noses and mouths are masked.

*

Hebei has China's worst air pollution. Shahe is one of its major sources of pollution.

(*South China Morning Post*, September 2017)

*

> Air Quality: Purple. Very unhealthy.
> All groups may experience serious health effects.

*

Factories in Shahe, the "City of Glass", produce about 160 million weight cases of flat glass annually, 20 per cent of all glass produced in China.

(*China Daily*, February 2017)

*

etched, aluminium, float, sheet, green, blue, gold, pink, grey mirror, marble, reflective, patterned, clear, tempered, louvre, jalousie, silver, turquoise, cobalt, terrazzo, garden, painted

*

Sand is the raw material in glass production. The factories are surrounded by fields. The fields are lined with corn. The corn is coated in sand.

*

The   Sandman   is   coming.

*

She said, Go on, try it. Tip your head back, drink bitter air.

*

Smog, *n.* 2. *fig.* A state or condition of obscurity or confusion; something designed to confuse or obscure.

(*Oxford English Dictionary*)

*

Oxford, UK.
Air Quality: Green. Good.
Ideal for outdoor activities.

*

Hear no evil.   See no evil.   Breathe no evil.

*

Populations in low-income cities are the most impacted by polluted air.

(World Health Organisation Ambient Air Quality Database, 2018)

*

Little drops of water,
Little grains of sand
Make the mighty ocean
and the pleasant land.

("Little Things", Julia A. F. Carney, *Gospel Teacher*, c. 1845)

*

The thick white steam pumped
into blast-furnace clouds is
almost beautiful.

*

FICTION

LOVE FROM A KNIFE

KATIE WILLIS

B ack in the day, before the soldiers. Before, before, when there were all-night orchestras and fireworks, and all the tomatoes you could eat, this island was a soft warm place. Then, a grown woman, barely five feet tall, hurled herself off Rook Cliff over on the east side because she saw the war coming deep inside her tiny little head. She knew that war, wild war, rips the sinews from you. It makes you slip low and froth at the mouth.

That woman was related to me. She was a third cousin once removed. I never danced on her makeshift grave, but I took ownership of her second-hand bike, making it third-hand and floral. I twisted all kinds of island wildflowers around the blue handlebars. I had a different name back then, but the soldiers took it from me, not telling me why.

"Your name will melt in our hands. You will forget yourself." That's all they said.

When I woke up, I was almost eighteen and the bike and the wildflowers were gone. I chose a new girl name, and as I did, something bloomed open inside my chest. I knew so much could be vanished in the dark teeth of war: the pine trees, the heather, the rivers and the sea. My new name was indivisible beauty and from the start, I knew not to speak it aloud to anyone.

Two days ago, on the north side of the island, I saw a knife wedged into the soil like an arrow pointing the way to battle. I knew it belonged to one of the soldiers. It had the trademark rivets on the handle. The earth, dry as a peach, and me, a scavenger, with no moss left to stroke. I heard the soil moan when I scooped it up. I did what the sun used to do; I pressed firmly. I had my limits, but I was strong. The lustre of the blade! I could slip my whole body into it where I was broken. When I think of a knife, I imagine it can cut a chunk out of the moon, and who wouldn't want to do that. Girls and knives go together like an electrical storm. One of them is lightning and one of them is thunder.

Yesterday, over by Strait's Hollow, I found myself a narrowboat. That place is not for everyone. It still carries the smell of wasted soldiers, a wad of lawless bodies springing up like hogweed, thrust-punching the ground by day in their knee-high boots, howling like hyenas at night.

My boat, my boat. It was resting in the dry river on planks of softly rotting wood. I came at it kissing the blade of my knife. I was fierce inside, bundled up, ragged, bubbling all over from the northern wind. I pulled my trench coat tight across my blouse and skirt, trying to keep out every smudge of cold. Carefully I slid my knife inside my coat, inside the waistband of my skirt so the icy steel of it marked me.

I ran at my boat like it was a goshawk. I love the wings on a goshawk.

"I'm getting the dirt from your bones," I whispered.

Boats have bone parts to them, and those parts are there for the licking. I put my tongue to my boat, tasting the rust on it. I kissed around the cracked and missing windows smashed on the floor inside, like clumps of rock salt. I cursed the soldiers for that.

There was little inside: an upturned bucket, coils of old rope with weeds growing from their knots, creeping towards me. In the corner, a bird was a mere fistful of wings when I picked it up and threw it out. I waited for a moment, and, in the waiting, I caught my breath.

When you curl up inside a boat, it becomes yours. I named my new boat *Valerie*, for the ten months of war she'd endured.

"With a knife and a boat, I'll be free," I murmured.

Some things come into your life. Some things pass on. In that moment, I was a current of hope.

On my boat, I was looking sideways and backwards at life. It was just me, my soul and my knife. I closed my eyes, remembered the gentle print of rain on skin and cried out. That gentleness! Something, someone, touching you where you needed it most.

I was complete with a knife. Full of grace. I was never afraid of it; I had a greedy heart. We are good together, I thought. We are some kind of perfect match. I knew I could love a girl from a knife. Love her under electric stars and save her from the soldiers.

"In the name of all that is left on this island, please give me a girl to climb on," I shouted.

That feeling of climbing is like walking barefoot through thick heather. It's pulling the light from the sky.

When the night came, I lay down beneath a glut of stars and a tiny padlock moon. At first, I was listening out for the voices of soldiers. It's always best to be wary. If you went right down to the sea that the soldiers drained, you'd find a moth-red womb that opens up from the depths of it, and a growing voice that urges, *Don't fight away the land. Don't go down silently. Live the life you were meant to live.*

In the morning I woke to bitter cold, the kind that slots right inside bone, turning you out of yourself. Strait's Hollow gave off an early-day humming sound, slick and grey. Grey was the sound of a distant glacier cracking. Grey was the taste of silence. There were no animals. Even the puny wolves had left.

"Are you looking upon our new home kindly?" I asked of my knife. And I stroked it the way I wanted to stroke a girl's inner thigh, bedding her down with lover's talk.

It was close to three this afternoon, when I saw something precious waltzing about in a long grey coat. Grey again, but the shade of hope, of promise. I saw two short-booted feet rolling around in shingle. That had to be my girl! As she came closer, I saw that there was a wildness in her left eye, like a jabbering dream. That was the moment I fell in love with her.

"I am nine people's memories, and then some," she said, looking across at me.

"That's some heavy weight," I replied. I blew her a kiss because I thought her body needed it, but I wasn't quite ready to take her aboard.

Her head was a tipping point. She rubbed away at her hip-bone and cursed some of her inside parts. Machine parts, she called them.

"I am missing most of my spleen. And my liver doesn't work so well because it's swollen like a pig's bladder."

There was nothing I could say to that, so I started to unfasten the top buttons of my blouse in solidarity.

She told me she was searching for a church because she had something inside her that needed praying out. I understood. I knew that when you put your lips around something, the sharp trapped pieces inside just fall away.

"The island's church is gone," I said. "The soldiers ripped it down."

I watched her rub a hole right through her grey coat and floral skirt to her hipbone as she listened to me talk on about churches. I told her that being in a church is like lying on your front porch and drinking sloe gin. And that sometimes the secret parts of a church, the ones by the altar, smelled like almonds, and that in itself was a strange thing.

"I'm thinking of making my boat into a church," I said.

She told me how she loved a church like a mountain range because the peak and the pulpit were the same and no tall belligerent solider could tell her otherwise.

"Churches have me wanting to touch parts of myself," I muttered to her. "They have me thinking of who I could become."

She looked at me and unbuttoned her coat so the flowers on her skirt billowed like a sheet on a line. She was magical. She was enough. She was almost too much for me. With her hands on her hips, she told me that some days she felt poured out over her feet. That having broken machine parts inside wasn't necessarily a death sentence.

"Amen to that," I said, taking her hand and pulling her aboard *Valerie*.

We sat side by side on the deck. My girl was tight and beautiful. She had some small burnishings to her, some glistening gold threads on the sleeves of her coat. Many flowers stretched across her skirt as though the wind was pushing at them. What I really wanted lay beneath, under that sloped wildflower meadow. In that moment I started making plans for us. I told her that I knew more about sadness than a girl my age should, and that was mostly because of the soldiers.

I brushed her with my knife where it didn't matter much, on a small red poppy on her skirt, close to the hem.

"Don't get inside too soon," she said, and she laughed.

She took hold of my hand and kissed the knuckles on it. She was soft-mouthed and effervescent.

"Aren't you too small to carry a knife?" she asked.

"Never," I replied. And I wanted so much to climb her body and rest deep inside her.

I looked into her eyes and demanded to know her name.

"Ace. But I never want you speaking it," she said.

"Is it your born name?"

"Of course," she replied.

Any name is really just a ribbon of weeds because there is a space into which you walk where the naming doesn't matter. Where the sadness that has flooded you, passes off and away, and you have a knife and a whole new girl to love.

I turned to her and touched her wrist with the blade of my knife. Just a small touch, like a bee sting, and she was all over it, shouting and loving me.

"A blessing, you crazy knife girl. A beauty, for sure. For sure, a blessed beauty," she said.

She came close to the side of me, hitching up her wide skirt.

Rolling her tongue to lick the bow of her top lip, she whispered, "Salt and scrubland."

These were her favourite things. They were her splinters of light. They were the surges of electricity starting her heart. And I wanted her more, more, more.

Holding my knife under my chin, closing my eyes tight, I leaned in towards one of her favourite things: the scrubland on the far side of the island that still had a bit of colour to it, a deep rust colour which the rain made juice of. I moved past scrubland, past fallen pine trees, past soldier harm. Something powerful was happening, I knew it. Something was reaching up to grow.

"I don't want to break into your body," I whispered back.

She lifted a foot and curled her body into the freeze of me. She ran her fingers through my tangled hair.

My head was a ball of fire. I threw my knife up in the air and cried out. She loved me for the sound I made.

My knife was joy. When it came down, I put it tender, beloved, up against my chest, and I rocked it. From my boat, from my knife, a love-girl had come to speak to the forgotten fragments of me. *Come home. You're safe. Come home and love. Remember.*

I handed her my knife. It was time.

The kiss she gave me as a thank-you tasted good. It was the memory of wet icing sugar. I'd loved that sweet stickiness before the soldiers came. I swallowed bits of her right then.

"I like to lie down on a hard surface for love," she said. "Love can be two parts peace and three parts rough, you know."

I knew. I knew all about the love parts from the thinking and dreaming I'd done. Love is silt and flint. It's jasmine and a lighted window and rough hands pushing past the soldiers through the dark.

She put my knife to her heart. That's the way to put love in and take it out.

"I've never loved a girl, although I've always wanted to carry one down a hallway after supper," she said.

"Ace," I savoured softly.

"I told you not to say my name," she shouted.

I cried over on the right side, a little way from her, my legs busted up by my chest. You can curse me all you want; you can stick a rod through my thigh, but I will still love you, I thought. The smell of frangipani wafted in from somewhere. It was a memory smell. There was no frangipani left on the island now.

When night came, I asked her if she could locate Orion or any other constellations in the sky. She told me that perhaps she could, but she wasn't sure if she would because I was a girl with a tough rind who was scared as a cat inside.

"I never said I was scared."

"You didn't have to," she replied.

She said it was like the night of her cousin's wedding all over again, when she hid under the dressing table in her ruby-red tulle dress clutching a block-heeled shoe, saying that all she really wanted was to live alone and dance recklessly. She said I had a kind of look.

"What kind of look?" I asked.

"Like someone ate you up before you had a chance to live and love."

I took the knife back then.

"It's not yours to keep," I said.

"Are you a bit messed up?" she asked.

I told her that knives don't mess you up. They're like a mother when you need one, digging into the best parts of yourself. No one's alone. No one.

I kissed the blade on it and listened out for something.

The knife was telling me nothing.

There was no light in the darkness, but there was a light inside her. Two lights. Both of them shimmering softly under her blouse, to the right of her ribcage.

She smelled of woodsmoke and sherbet and I ran my knife along each side of her. I made her outline strong.

"Will you hold my elbow?" she asked.

She was getting sleepy.

"You like being touched there?"

"Before the war I used to dream of it."

There was a current in her that the soldiers hadn't killed off. I put my face to the bend of her elbow. I struck the air twice with my knife. The first strike, rich, for the time before the soldiers came. The second strike, raw, for the hope she had inside. I leaned across and made a diamond mark of love on her cheek with the blade.

"I need to know your name," she muttered.

She held her hands as though in prayer.

My knife was tender. She was tender too, her cheek, the dark silkiness of it! I forgot myself. I was looking and looking through the lights, at the body she had inside her clothes. It wasn't white like a lily. It wasn't the colour of saffron. It was something in between. In the looking, I held everything that ran through her, every bit of life she'd lived so far. Are we falling? I wondered. And if we are, who will catch us?

The sky was black, and it hummed, but we were not the night. Our world creaked.

"We are worth so much," I said.

Speaking is a kind of nourishing. As I spoke, I kissed her chin. I saw a field of daisies, both of us pulling off their petals and lining them up on the soft grass beside our bare feet.

Hunger is hunger. She was my girl. Between us was such peace. I thought of her breathing and thriving, her mouth moving softly as though she was sucking grains of rice. I brought my finger to her top lip and held it there, and I wondered if the sea was like a girl. I wondered if just thinking about something could fill it in where it was missing.

"Stay, and leave the leaving to the soldiers," I said.

I buried those words in her neck. There was a rhythm to her breathing that had me falling out of myself.

I started calling her my lovely. I started calling her my own to keep.

"You and you, sweetheart, and the marks I made on you," I whispered.

I touched her cheek. Slowly, slowly, I wrote my name right there. I wrote who I was and what we might become.

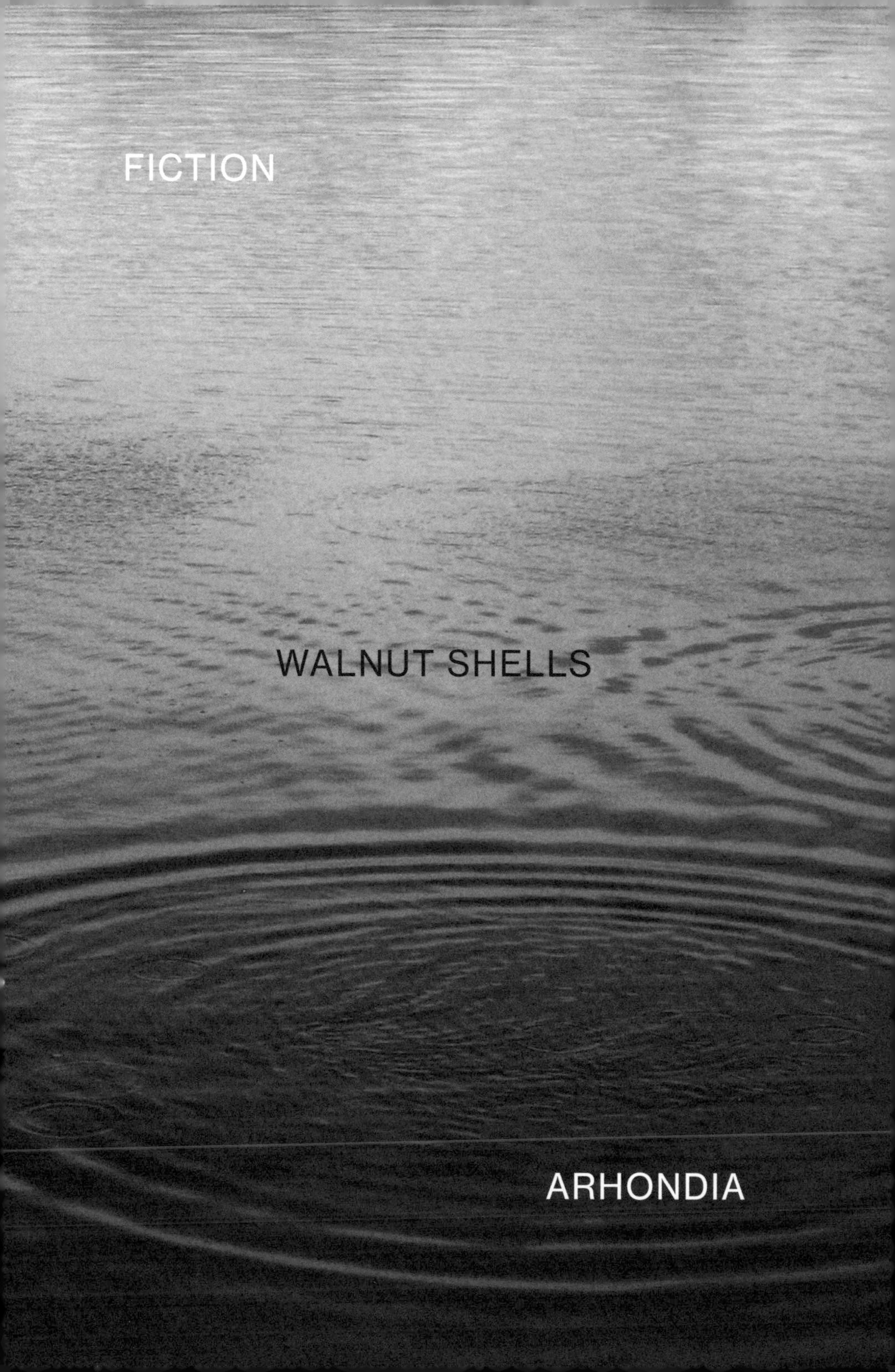

FICTION

WALNUT SHELLS

ARHONDIA

We'll make a fleet of walnut boats and own
every puddle in this city.

I woke up with the taste of milk in my mouth and the sound of rain drumming on the classroom windows. I had been dreaming of walnut shells made into tiny boats with the help of toothpicks, coloured threads and shreds of newspaper. My brother, Giorgos, was in the dream too. We were in the park, climbing into our tiny walnut-shell boats and setting sail in the puddles under the neradzi trees. The puddles swelled into a gushing river that let us float through all of Athens.

The buildings in Syntagma Square were immersed in the rising tide that was trying to swallow us all up. Parliament was still recognisable by its cream-and-white pediment, which wasn't yet fully submerged. The Greek flag stood on top of it, blowing crazily, as if it wanted to free itself from the pole and rip across the grey sky. The *Tsoliades* guards who always stand outside parliament were gone. We saw Babás swimming in the dark water. We shouted at him to get into our boats but he couldn't hear us. He kept swimming the other way.

All the children in the class were gathered above my head and Mrs Electra was telling them to stand back and give me air.

"Sophia, Sophia, can you hear me?" she asked.

"Sometimes we put melted wax in the bottom of the shell to make sure the wind doesn't topple it but my feet always get stuck," I said. Actually, this is what they told me I said.

Mrs Electra lifted me up like I was a princess in a fairy tale. This is something I remember myself. "I have to take Sophia to see the nurse," she said. "Aris, you will be in charge because you're the eldest. No one is allowed to go into the courtyard. It's two degrees and might snow later. The news said that today will be the coldest day in the last decade."

"What does 'decade' mean, Mrs Electra?" said Aris.

"My mamá says that when people feel bad the weather becomes bad like their feelings," said Kassandra, my best friend.

"Aris, a decade is what we call a period of ten years. Kassandra, thanks for that. Let's all try to think happy thoughts, then, and bring the sun back. Now, I want you all to sit at your desks and work on the letters delta and epsilon. When I come back I want every one of you to have written each letter twenty times. OK? Remember you're all in Year One now. This is not playschool, you are big children."

"Can I go with her? I can tell her a story my mamá tells me when I am not well," said Kassandra.

"No, Kassandra, Sophia needs to rest now. Maybe you can tell her a story later. Now please take your seat." With that, Mrs Electra put an arm around my shoulders and we walked slowly towards the little room at the end of the hallway where the sick children have to go.

She helped me lie down on the brown divan. There was a heater on the floor, right next to the bed, warming the room up but also making it smell strange. My stomach felt like it was trying to tie itself into a knot. We never turned the heating on in our house now, even when it got really cold. The nurse, Mrs Argyro, gave me some water and Mrs Electra sat next to me, holding my hand and asking me questions.

"Have you eaten this morning?"

"I've had milk."

"What did you eat yesterday?"

"We had milk. Mamá says a doctor told her it has everything we need. It's the best food in the world for growing children."

"Your mamá is right. Did you have anything other than milk?" said Mrs Electra, frowning and looking at Mrs Argyro as she spoke.

"Not yesterday."

"What about the day before, Sophia?"

"I can't remember. We have been saving money since Babá had to go away," I said, because I had a feeling I wasn't saying the right things and would get into trouble.

"Where did your babá go?"

"I don't know. He went for a walk with the two men that came to the house two weeks ago but he hasn't come back. Mamá says he is away for work and we have to save money so he can come back."

Mrs Electra and Mrs Argyro looked at each other. Then Mrs Argyro left and quickly came back with a paper bag that made the little room smell like a bakery.

"*Tyropita* or *spanakopita*?" said Mrs Electra.

"I don't have money for either," I said.

"Don't you worry, little one. You can have both if you can eat them," said Mrs Argyro.

"Yes, that will be your challenge. Do you think you can do it?" said Mrs Electra.

"What if I start them and can't finish?"

"Have as much of them as you can eat and don't worry," said Mrs Argyro, pursing her lips together as if she was trying to stop any more words coming out. She handed me the paper bag with the two *pitas*. The spinach *pita* was shaped like a snail shell made of golden filo pastry. The one with the cheese was plain and shaped like a rectangle and sprinkled with sesame seeds. I picked the cheese one first. It was crunchy and warm and the inside was full of salty melted feta. My stomach let out a big gurgling sound.

"Is that the sound of an approving tummy?" said Mrs Electra.

I nodded, taking another bite and letting crumbs jump out of my mouth onto my jumper. I noticed that my shoes were off and had been placed just in front of the little divan I was sitting on. I couldn't remember having them removed. They looked dirty and made me feel small. My socks were old, their colour was a greying kind of white and darker around the toes, and they made me feel even smaller. Mrs Electra's shoes were wine-coloured and very shiny. They were shoes to be proud of. She was wearing tights. I'm sure they would be perfect around the toes.

"Eat up, sweetheart. We're trying to call your mamá so she can come and pick you up. Mrs Argyro has got you some orange juice to have with your pies."

"She won't answer the phone. She never answers numbers she doesn't know. In case it's someone we owe money to. Just send her a text."

They looked at each other again. Once they got out the door they said something about me being thin, something about shopping and something about Mamá. I started chewing with my mouth open, really loudly, so I couldn't hear them any more.

During the last week we hadn't even gone to Santa Claus for food. He cooks in a big pot, on the street, in the middle of Athens, and feeds anyone who is hungry. He does it every day. Giorgos and I think he might be related to Santa, but his beard is not white, it's black. Maybe he is Santa's young son and he's training for the job. Every time we go, while we are queuing I think of asking him, but he will think it's a very silly question if he's not, and when we reach him he's always in a rush, so I just take my food and go. Mamá says he probably is related. He sings *Mia zoi tin ehoume* while he serves the food and makes everyone smile.

I fell asleep without finishing the *pitas*. Mrs Electra and Mrs Argyro came back bringing Mamá with them and woke me up from my dream. Santa with the dark beard was in a walnut boat and he was trying to help Babá out of the cold dark water but Mamá started talking and I had to leave the dream before he saved him. She looked like she'd been crying. I told her I had something to eat, which made her close her eyes and take a deep breath.

"I am sorry, Sophia, so very sorry," she said, hugging me until my skin felt like it was being squeezed onto my bones. "Pappous is coming from Mani, bringing lovely food with him."

Mrs Electra wouldn't know that Mamá, Babás and Pappous were always arguing since the coffee shop in Ermou Street closed down. Pappous would shout at them that the coffee shop had closed because Babás handled things badly. Mamá and Babás would shout back that they had done everything they could to keep it open. Everyone ended up swearing, banging doors and sometimes breaking ashtrays, cups and vases. They always told Giorgos and me to go to our rooms but that didn't make any difference. We could still hear their shouting.

I hope Babás comes back, even if they argue again. Maybe he left because he is mad at all of us for not taking his side in the arguments.

Babás always set off for work many hours before I went to school so he could make coffees for people before they opened their shops or started their office jobs. He even delivered coffees straight to their desk. He used to be very tired when he came home.

Mrs Electra took Mamá away to talk to her some more and I stayed with Mrs Argyro who told me to lie down and continue to rest, even though I told her that I felt much better after the pies and a nap.

I was bored and asked if I could go back to class. She insisted I keep lying down. I closed my eyes and tried to go back into the dream I was having about black-beard Santa. I could bring the images back in my memory but nothing moved. Everything was still. The walnut boats just sat there. As if sleeping was what made the water run and objects have a purpose.

Eventually Mamá came back holding my schoolbag and coat.

"Is Giorgos coming with us?"

"No, Mrs Electra will bring him home later," said Mamá.

"Can you please give these to my brother? I couldn't finish them," I said, handing Mrs Electra the pies I'd saved for him.

"You keep those and eat them when you get home. There are two more for Giorgos," said Mrs Electra with smiley lips but dark eyes.

Mamá told Mrs Electra and Mrs Argyro she was sorry, again.

We took the long way home and went via Ermou Street. Mamá had to go into our coffee shop and get some papers that Babás needed. It was still raining and I could feel my socks getting wet in my shoes.

"Has he come back? Is he waiting at home?"

"No, he is still away but hopefully he will be back soon."

"Where is he?"

"He just had to go and talk to the two men who came to the house, about business."

"Are they going to help him open our café again?"

"I don't think so."

"Why not?"

"Enough questions, Sophia!"

I preferred how she was in front of Mrs Argyro and Mrs Electra.

Mamá unlocked the shop door and flicked the light switch but the lights didn't go on. It was dark, as though we were inside a shadow of our old shop. I felt like I did in my dream, only this time I couldn't float away. I sat on one of the chairs, took the pies out of my schoolbag and pinched off a small piece of the spinach one. I began to worry that someone was hiding behind the bar where Babás used to make the coffees. Maybe one of the men that took him away was there and he would try to take Mamá too. I got up and waited close to the door so I could run away and shout for help if I needed to.

The tables were dusty. Even though it was dark I could see the layer of dirty fluff that was gathering everywhere.

Mamá got the papers from under the silent red till and we left. As she was locking up, I noticed that the shoe shop next door had also closed down. Only one pair of shoes, dark-blue velvet, strappy, remained in the window, with its price right in front of it. €49.99. I wondered whether they'd sold everything else or had just forgotten to take this pair. Mr Panagiotis and Mrs Mika. They always spoke to me when I helped Babá in the coffee shop. Maybe the men took them and the shoes away too. I didn't know why they'd left these velvet ones. I would have worn them if they'd given them to me instead of leaving them in the window.

We walked down Ermou Street. All the shops that Babá used to deliver coffees to had closed down as well. Some were empty and dark and you could see little bits of what they used to sell inside. Others had shutters pulled down that someone had drawn graffiti over. The words *EUROPE VASANIZOME* took up two closed shops' shutters.

"What does 'Europe *vasanizome*' mean, Mamá?"

"The person who wrote that is trying to tell Europe that they are being tortured."

"What is 'tortured'?"

"When someone does something painful to you and they won't stop."

"Are we being tortured? Is someone doing something painful to us?"

"I don't know. I don't think anyone important is going to see this. It's pointless," Mamá said, walking on quickly through the rain.

A few doors down a shutter had been painted with an ancient Greek statue throwing a flaming euro sign in the air.

"What's that?" I said to Mamá.

"A Molotov bomb."

"What's a Molotov bomb?"

"Can we just get home, Sophia? We're getting wet and we'll both catch a cold," said Mamá, speeding up until we were almost running through the rain. My shoes had changed colour from the water and squeaked when I walked. My socks felt all sticky around my feet.

"I think you're making it rain," I said and stopped walking.

"What are you talking about? Walk or you'll be wet to the bone."

"You're making it rain. Kassandra's mamá says people's moods affect the weather."

"Walk!"

"I don't want to walk."

"You're being a brat. Just walk," said Mamá, pulling me down the street.

"I left the pies in the café. I'm still hungry," I screamed at the top of my voice.

The few people on the street stared as they hurried past, hunched under their black umbrellas.

Mamá turned and looked at me. She crouched down and hugged me.

"I'm so sorry, Sophia. I'm trying. I keep getting it wrong. I love you, very much. Darling, we need to get home so you can rest. Please."

We walked the remainder of the way in silence. Hondos, where Mamá used to buy her perfume at Christmas, was still open. Marks and Spencer, the big English shop, was open too but we never went in there. They had their own café. It would be a good place to buy new socks if we had the money.

When we got home I took off all my wet clothes and put on my pyjamas. Mrs Electra arrived with Giorgos soon afterwards and Mamá told me to go to my room. Very few lights were on and the house was getting dark. All sorts of blue colours rested on everything as though the evening was putting a veil over every corner. It felt even colder.

Mrs Electra had three shopping bags with her and a card that Kassandra had made for me. There was a big yellow sun in the middle of it, which said: *Come back to class, I miss you. I think the weather is bad because I am sad. Bring back the sun.* It was written in Mrs Electra's handwriting. We didn't know how to write big sentences yet.

I wasn't sure I wanted to bring the sun back. Without the rain I would have nowhere to float my walnut boats. Unless I went to the sea, but I didn't think anyone was going to be taking me to the sea. I put the card on my bedside table. Kassandra had definitely made the sun herself. It had a smiley face on it.

The doorbell rang again and I heard Pappous' voice. He walked through the house and straight to my room.

"My little Sophia, how are you?" he said, and sat down on the edge of my bed. He was wearing a woolly orange jumper. When Yiayia was alive she always used to knit bright-coloured jumpers. She said a bright colour helped keep us warm in the winter.

Pappous put his index finger to his lips to show me I had to keep a secret. Then he took five large ION chocolates with almonds out of the case he had with him and put them into my hands. I smiled. They were my favourite.

"Hide them, they are just for you," he said and gave me a big smile that showed all his teeth, including the gold one on the right side of his mouth. Suddenly everything became brighter. It was as though the colours of the house had changed.

"Can I have some now?" I whispered.

He shushed me but nodded and then gave me the big smile with all his teeth showing again. I love it when he smiles like that. It makes me feel clever.

"Did you bring something for Giorgos?" I said.

"For my namesake? Of course! Giorgos," he called out.

Giorgos came running in and Pappous took a large cloth bag out of his suitcase. When he opened it both Giorgos and I let out a scream. The bag was full, fit to burst, with walnuts. We could make all the boats we wanted. Hundreds of little boats. We would build a fleet of them. All the children in the neighbourhood could play.

"But first we have to crack them carefully," said Pappous.

"Yes, so the shells don't break," Giorgos and I cried out in unison.

"I was dreaming about them this morning when I fainted in school," I said.

"I know. A little bird told me, so I made sure I brought as many walnuts as I could find," he said, and smiled, but this time none of his teeth were on show. "Do you know the best thing about walnuts?" Pappous continued.

"No," Giorgos and I said, looking at him.

"They are the kind of food that makes our brain work better."

"So, every time we eat them we get clever?" I said.

"Exactly."

"You get clever and can make a better boat!" said Giorgos, making Pappous laugh.

"Now, I'll crack some open so you can start thinking about the boats you're going to make. Then I have to go and talk to your mamá. She's making lentil stew in the kitchen, so we'll be eating in a while. You two stay here and start collecting what you want to use for sails."

Giorgos and I looked at each other. Everyone was walking off to talk all the time.

"I'm going to find out what's going on," Giorgos said.

"I'm coming too."

"No, you'll make a noise and get us caught."

"I won't, I promise."

"OK, but you have to do everything I do, and quickly," he said.

We opened my bedroom door and listened. It sounded like Mrs Electra was still there and Mamá was talking to Pappous. Mrs Electra was making sounds like she agreed with everything Mamá said. Giorgos inched slowly, very close to the walls so the light from the street lamps outside didn't make shadows on the floor that would give us away. After a few steps he turned and looked at me, pointing at the floorboard that creaked. We both stepped over it and were as close to the kitchen door as we could get without revealing ourselves.

"You are either too proud or completely stupid," said Pappous.

"Is that all you have to say to me after everything I told you?"

"Let's all calm down. This is a difficult situation," said Mrs Electra.

I wished she didn't have to see Mamá and Pappous arguing.

"My daughter's first priority should be her children's well-being. Sophia and Giorgos starving will only make things worse. Why did you not call me immediately? How are you going to even try and fix this without my help?"

"I am in touch with a lawyer," said Mamá.

"And the children? You're giving them milk and taking them to a guy who cooks for the homeless for their dinner. Sophia had to faint from hunger in school before you called me."

"I panicked. I have had a very hard couple of weeks. I should have called you. We can't even afford the lights we have on in the kitchen. We can't afford to cook in this house."

"Your mother always treated you like a baby and you remained one. You are not fit to have children. Go be a cleaner if you don't have money. Earn some wages and put food on the table."

"The court case is in three days' time and the lawyer is going to try and convince the judge that Spyros has no intention of running away and not paying his debt to the state. He wants to convince him that Spyros will work to pay every last cent. I have gathered whatever money I could find and have it ready to give to the lawyer." Mamá started to cry.

"You have money, here? In this house? And the children are fainting at school?"

The only sound coming out of the kitchen was Mamá's sobbing. When Pappous spoke again he sounded even more angry.

"You have lost your mind. I am taking the children with me to the village tonight."

"You have no right," said Mamá.

"I have no right? Ask your friend the teacher. You are negligent, you can't bring them up. You and your idiot husband are neglecting them. They are stick thin with dark circles under their eyes. You have money for the court but you don't care if the children suffer? You bitch!"

We heard the sound of a slap and a gasp. Then silence.

Mrs Electra spoke. "Mr Giorgos, please. Let's all discuss this calmly. The children are a wall away. Please!"

"You love your husband more than you love your children, you stupid bitch. What are you doing, walking around Athens longing for him while they are starving? It's a bad woman that does that. Once you are a mother, your children come first."

"You were never father of the year. Mamá was always on her own."

"You never fainted from hunger! I am taking the children right now and if you try to stop me I will report you to the police for neglect. Giorgos, Sophia, come here," shouted Pappous.

Giorgos and I froze, looking at each other in panic. We waited, breath held, counted to five with our fingers and then opened the door.

Mamá started screaming for Pappous to stop. There were no tears now but her face was turning red. Pappous yelled at us to go get our things. Mrs Electra stood up and put her hands together as though she was praying. She was begging him to stop. Mamá continued screaming and I didn't know what to do. I just held my brother's hand and stared at all of them. I felt something warm running all the way down my leg. Then Mrs Electra shouted so loud she covered everyone else's voice.

"Enough! This is no way to act in front of children. I will bring the authorities down on both of you if you don't behave."

Pappous and Mamá looked at me and the pool I had created on the floor and stopped making any sounds. My brother let my hand go and I realised my legs were shaking.

Mrs Electra took me to the bathroom to clean me up. The house was very quiet. For the first time since she'd arrived I felt glad to have Mrs Electra around. When we went back into the front room, Pappous was in the kitchen asking Mamá if she wanted some wine he'd brought from the village.

Giorgos and I said good night and were taken to our rooms by Mrs Electra. Once the large hand on the clock in Giorgos' room had moved fifteen times we went back into the hallway.

The first thing we heard was the faint sound of wine falling into a glass. Mamá must have finished the first glass Pappous gave her. None of them spoke for a while. Then Pappous said:

"I don't agree with how things are done in this house but your husband is not a bad man. I am not naive. He does not deserve to be in a cell."

"He's in a cell with fifteen other men," said Mamá.

"I understand. The *krisi* has put many honest men in prison when the real crooks are untouched. His debt to the state is not that big. We will all help to pay it. I will ask everyone I know in the village. There is nothing to be ashamed of. Fifty euros here, a hundred euros there, we'll find the money. I don't know when but we will find it. Don't worry."

Giorgos and I looked at each other. We didn't speak. I could see Giorgos' eyes watering but he didn't cry. He swallowed the air four times and his chest started going up and down.

Prison is a place for bad people. Why did the men that came to the house take Babá to prison? If only they'd talked to me and Giorgos, we could have told them that he is a very good man.

I pulled Giorgos by the hand and we walked backwards towards my bedroom as quietly as possible. My heart was beating in my ears. If they found us they would know that we had heard. I didn't want to talk about Babás being in prison.

In the bedroom we sat on the floor cracking walnuts and eating them. We set the spoiled shells to one side and the shells that were perfect in front of us. Soon there were five rows of perfect walnut shells ready to be turned into boats.

"If we could change size and sail in the boats we could go and save Babás," I said.

"Don't be stupid," Giorgos said. "People don't change size. I'm tired of playing with your silly fake boats all the time. You're such a baby." He got up and stamped on the walnut shells until there were only tiny pieces all over the floor.

"Giorgos, stop, please stop." I put my arms out to protect our fleet of boats. He lifted his foot and stamped on my left hand. It felt like something cracked and I let out a scream, tears starting to run down my face even though I was trying to stop them so I wouldn't get him into trouble. Giorgos heard the sound my hand made and stood motionless, looking worried.

"I'm sorry. Please don't tell Mamá and Pappous," he said and ran out of the room crying.

I stayed on the floor and brushed all the broken shells to one side with my right hand because my left hand was hurting too much. One little walnut boat had slipped under the bed and saved itself. I would have to make myself smaller later, in my dream, and sail away on my own. I wished sleep would come down with the rain that kept going outside. I wanted to escape.

I put a toothpick with blue thread wrapped around it in the walnut boat to make the mast. A tiny piece of newspaper glued to the toothpick was my sail. The boat was manned by a captain I'd moulded from a paper clip. His brown hat was a bit of old jumper I stuck on the point I'd decided was his head. I named him Odysseus because Mrs Electra told us that was the name of the man with the most adventures in Greek mythology. Maybe he could save Babás.

That night I slept with the little walnut boat on my pillow but I dreamt of nothing but the rain.

NON-FICTION

BORN HUNGRY

HANNAH AUSTIN

I was born hungry. I don't mean that as a cute metaphor; I mean literally. My birthweight was 10 lb 2 oz (sorry, Mum). The gobsmacked midwives passed my podgy body between them like a cake in a game of "guess the weight", and my appetite for milk to fill my plus-sized belly was insatiable.

The doctors instructed Mum to feed me on demand – a practice Mum continued throughout my chubby childhood. My sister, Fran, and I were raised on a strict diet of frozen food: Findus crispy pancakes (pockets of batter stuffed with tongue-annihilating cheesy lava, if you haven't had the pleasure), turkey drummers, potato waffles – anything that took fifteen minutes to defrost in the oven. Even if she'd known how to, Mum didn't have time between her day and evening jobs to cook from scratch for two screaming kids, who'd be happier anyway with anything processed, battered and slathered in ketchup. I don't blame her. As for Dad, he could barely burn toast, and was rarely around to do so.

"I'm still hungryyy," I whined one night in front of the TV, meaning: *I want sugar.*

"Have a bowl of cereal, then, love," Mum said, like I knew she would. Before she'd even finished her sentence, I was flying off the couch and into the kitchen, where Dad sat at the table reading the paper. On my tiptoes, I liberated the neon box of Coco Pops from their home between Dad's boring Bran Flakes and Mum's fat-free, sugar-free, fun-free Special K. I poured myself a huge fix of the chocolate kiddie crack and shovelled the first gorgeous spoonful into my mouth. Bliss.

Dad, who'd been slurping tea (two sugars) from a chipped mug and staring at me the whole time, said: "So you want to end up like Auntie Eira, then, do you?"

I froze mid-chew. He was looking at me funny – like I was a stranger, or a specimen.

"Do you? Answer me, then!"

"No, Dad," I managed in a tiny voice. The chocolate sop in my mouth no longer tasted like heaven. It tasted like shame. I forced myself to swallow, but the lump in my throat remained.

"Well that's where you'll end up if you carry on eating that shite."

I burst out crying and ran up to the bedroom I shared with Fran, leaving my bittersweet bowl of betrayal crackling on the kitchen side. No, no, *no* – I *didn't* want to end up like Auntie Eira, Dad's only sister, who was fat and disgusting, who couldn't get a man, who no one liked and who had brought it all on herself. I might've been only nine years old, but I already knew that Auntie Eira was the worst possible place to end up.

I was bullied a little for my chubbiness throughout school, although it faded into irrelevance compared to the bullying I faced when I was diagnosed as "gifted" and skipped a school year (aged ten); or when I developed bald patches from trichotillomania, a rare psychological disorder characterised by urges to pull out your own hair (aged twelve); or when I was outed as queer (aged fourteen). Still, I'd occasionally starve myself, delighted if I could manage just an apple a day, and the rage I felt at my chunky thighs sometimes erupted into punching them until they were bruised purple, green, black. When I discovered feminism, via a riot grrrl mix tape my first girlfriend made me (aged fifteen), it wasn't a moment too soon.

I'm thirty-four now, and I've worked hard to achieve a fairly healthy body image – for a woman. But what does "for a woman" mean? Mum has yo-yo dieted all her life, and still calls herself "naughty" when she has a chocolate biscuit from her "treats cupboard". Fran and her friends have regular weight-loss fads in which they replace every meal with a low-calorie shake. Most of my partners have had eating disorders. And my best friend is obsessed with her weight – at six feet tall she resents being bigger than most men, less fragile, taking up more space.

Like everyone, I've grown up in a climate in which women's bodies – and especially our weight – are relentlessly scrutinised. And, like everyone, I internalised everything I was taught about fatness – and especially fat women – by my family. I'm from Wales, where 65 per cent of men and 53 per cent of women are either overweight or obese. I'm also from typically Welsh stock: our family is short, densely muscled, built for mining coal and ploughing fields, with a love of food and booze that exacerbates a genetic predisposition towards girth.

By the somewhat controversial measurement of body mass index (BMI), my sister and I carry a little extra weight, albeit not enough to remark on. I carry most of mine on my hips, tits and arse – the socially sanctioned sites for female fat. My weight has been remarkably consistent since my late teens, apart from a few years in my early twenties, when my narcotic diet of pills and powders melted the pounds away (and my innocent family dished out double helpings of praise).

At his heaviest, Dad (who's about 5' 7") was 18 stone. A fair bit of that was rugby muscle, but a lot of it was fat. Despite his incessant boozing, he keeps the weight off now with daily workouts, regular charity-fundraising exercise missions (the Three Peaks Challenge, that kind of madness) and his wife Janine's healthy cooking. Dad's older brothers fall into the "morbidly obese" BMI category – but they're big, strapping blokes, ex-rugby players (our national religion); they're *meant* to take up space. And, apart from jokes about Uncle Llew's cheese habit and gentle ribbing about beer bellies, they escape the constant barrage of criticism directed towards Auntie Eira.

I moved across enemy lines from Wales to England a couple of years ago. Dad likes to make the most of my rare visits to the motherland by drinking even more than usual and talking late into the night.

"Your Auntie Eira," he slurred on my latest visit, swaying slightly on his sofa where I sat between him and my partner, Jo. "Now *she*'s a big girl."

"Big girl" is South Wales vernacular for "morbidly obese". It has no male equivalent.

"I suppose so, Dad," I said, hoping we could leave it at that, as if he ever left it at that.

"You *suppose so*?" He shot me what I think was meant to be an expression of disbelief, rendered slightly comical by his dark eyes' failure to focus on mine. "Come on, Hannah, she's bloody *massive*. And she promised your nan she'd sort herself out. Did you know that? Nan's dying wish, that was."

Nan had also been a "big girl". She struggled with her weight all her life, serving up mountains of roast dinner for her family and a butterless baked potato for herself every Sunday, though I never noticed her actually losing weight. As a child, I was fascinated by the way her ankles bulged over her sandals, and she gave the best cuddles – soft, pillowy, all-encompassing – like being hugged by a billowing cloud.

"I'm telling you straight," Dad continued. "Your nan begged Eira to lose weight – on her deathbed, mind, this was, at the hospital – and Eira cried and promised she would. But look at her – she's even bigger than Nan was at her biggest! It was all barefaced bloody *lies*."

"Oh come on, Dad. It's not like she *meant* to lie to Nan. She's tried a million times to lose weight. It's just not that easy, is it?"

"Of course it is – just stop fucking eating! Have some self-control, for God's sake."

He leaned forward and poured his millionth glass of wine.

Dad told us a lot about Eira that night, but he told us far more about himself.

He told us that if Eira suddenly becomes unemployed, or after she retires, he won't allow her to move in with their dad – my gramps. Dad and his siblings bought Nan and Gramps' ex-council house years ago under Thatcher's social-housing-decimating Right to Buy scheme, but the brothers own bigger shares than Auntie Eira, who works as a hotel receptionist for minimum wage and lives in a flat on the hotel grounds. You'd have thought such a move would be a good idea all round – Gramps had had a couple of falls in his house following a recent release from hospital – but apparently not.

"I want you and Fran to have my share of that house after I go," Dad said.

"That's sweet of you, Dad, but we've both got our own places. Auntie Eira would need your share much more than we would."

"I don't care. It's for you, not her."

"But she'd have nowhere to go! Would you seriously rather your own sister be homeless than live with your dad?"

"Yes," he said, not missing a beat.

He told us Eira had accompanied him to visit Gramps in hospital over the last couple of months. When they got to reception and found out his ward was at the opposite end of the sprawling complex, it became clear that she couldn't walk there unassisted. She'd wanted to use one of the hospital's wheelchairs, but Dad downright refused to push her in one, because: "She's not disabled, she's fat." I don't know how she got to Gramps' ward on that or subsequent visits.

He told us that Eira sometimes leaves her dirty coffee cups in Gramps' kitchen sink after visiting, or leaves a few of her possessions lying around if she's staying the night – which she does regularly, cooking and cleaning and keeping Gramps company. The disgust in Dad's voice was palpable; he spat these words out like they were curdling in his mouth. The clear implication was that she was *fat and lazy* – two traits that our culture, which equates fatness with immorality, insists are intertwined. And what's worse than laziness to a man so enamoured with the Protestant work ethic that he's tried and failed to retire three times?

"Sometimes," Dad continued, "– and I know this is bad – but sometimes, when we're out in public, I feel really ... *embarrassed.*"

"Embarrassed of what?" I said.

"Embarrassed to be seen with her. Embarrassed in case someone assumes she's my wife or something."

He's ashamed to be seen with his own sister in public in case someone he's never met thinks he's fucking her. That's how repulsed he is by his sister's body.

How obsessed, you might say, because all repulsion requires an element of fixation. It's all he sees about her; all he's ever spoken of in relation to her. To him, she is only and always an unruly, overflowing, uncontrolled body. No dreams or desires, hopes or ambitions, likes or dislikes, wishes or regrets, tastes or prejudices, secrets or plans, fears or phobias, ideals or values, friends or enemies, loves or losses, favourite songs or films or books or memories or places or people.

No personality.

No humanity.

Just fat.

But I don't know Auntie Eira's dreams or desires, either. I don't have that kind of relationship with her, or with my uncles. I moved away when I was eighteen, and, apart from Gramps, I only ever see my extended family at weddings, funerals, Christmases and the rare occasions when we happen to be visiting Gramps at the same time. Besides, my family is highly skilled at avoiding "deep talk" in favour of the wisecrack quip; at skimming life's surfaces rather than diving to its murky depths.

I feel closer to Eira than to my uncles, but only in the same way that I feel closer to most women than to most men – because I know what it means to be a woman in a patriarchal society. There are so many things I don't know about her – including whether the empathy I feel for her is mutual. I don't know her well enough to imbue her with the humanity I'm criticising Dad for failing to recognise. I may even be objectifying her further by insisting that she's more than just a body while being unable to tell you what else she is.

What I do know is this: It's impossible to weather a male-dominated climate in a female body without some level of erosion.

"But I think I'm a tidy bloke," was Dad's constant refrain that night on the couch – "tidy" being Welsh slang for "decent, good, upstanding". He seemed to know there was something wrong with the way he thought about his sister, and he was struggling to reconcile his perception of himself as a generally good man – which he is, in so many ways – with the fact that he held these views. Black-and-white thinking is something of a family speciality. He also seemed to be soliciting our opinions about these views – which Jo and I gave in no uncertain terms.

We pointed out the hypocrisy of Dad drinking himself into a stupor every night while couching his disgust about his sister's weight in alleged health concerns.

We pointed out the similarities between his arguments and those made by conservatives about gay men in the 1980s (they've brought AIDS on themselves by choosing immoral lifestyles; therefore, they don't deserve treatment; therefore, they deserve to die).

We pointed out the sheer weirdness of being so repulsed by, so fixated on, his sister's body.

We pointed out that most people overeat because of emotional problems, often trauma-related, and that it's more of an addiction than a conscious choice.

That it's nigh on impossible to eat well when you earn minimum wage, work night shifts, and lack both a garage to build a gym in and a culinarily knowledgeable wife to cook you balanced, healthy, nutritious meals.

That the cruel treatment she experiences at the hands of her brothers – the ones who are supposed to be on her side, to stick up for her in a world immeasurably crueller to her than it is to them – will only be making things worse.

That his embarrassment at being seen with her in public says far more about him than it does about her.

But there's always more that's left unsaid; more that's unsayable.

I didn't say: *You feel this way about your sister but not your brothers because Auntie Eira is female.*

I didn't say: *She repulses you because you believe a woman's main role in life is to look appealing to men.*

I didn't say: *Your feelings about her are a reflection of how you view all women.*

I didn't say: *When you insult Auntie Eira's body, I feel it as an assault against my own.*

Dad seemed to listen to us that night. He even seemed to realise a few things about himself. But I've seen that look before – a shaft of light threatening to pierce the clouds of alcohol in his eyes – and it's never preceded any meaningful change in his behaviour. And I've experienced such moments myself; the minor revelations that make up a lifetime of reflection. People always say I've got my dad's eyes.

The thing is, though, we're nowhere near as rational as we like to think. Self-awareness might be the new Holy Grail in our Age of Perpetual Mindfulness, but the mere act of realising something about yourself doesn't necessarily lead to changing it. If only. In my own personal Venn diagram, what I think and what I do are often two separate circles.

✳

Later that night, Dad went to the toilet while Jo and I put our coats on and said goodbye to Janine.

"Keep an eye on Dad," I whispered to Janine, concerned that perhaps we'd been a bit too honest with him. "Things got a bit heavy back there."

"Oh, you know what he's like, Han," she said, waving my concerns away. "He won't even remember it in the morning."

She was right. We saw him at Gramps' house the following day, where he didn't mention anything about the night before apart from to say he'd had a great time. I guess he couldn't have gone into it around Gramps, but there was no flicker of recognition hidden in his face (unlike Janine's knowing glances); no inkling that he'd heard what we'd said, or that we should talk about it again in the future. Nothing then, and nothing since.

None of us stayed at Gramps' long. I washed our dirty coffee cups and we went our separate ways – Janine to visit her mother in the nursing home, Dad to the pub, and Jo and I back to England.

We stopped for a guilty McDonald's en route home. I didn't even bother to remove the gherkin before devouring my quarter pounder and washing it down with a strawberry milkshake; I was desperate for some sweetness, however artificial. I taught myself to cook in my twenties, against the odds. I even eat pretentious things like kale these days – every nutritious frond tastes like class betrayal. But after that visit I was depleted; ravenous; starving for so many things. What can I say? I was born hungry.

POETRY

RUSHIKA WICK
TARQUIN LANDSEER
CAROL CAFFREY
LOUISA ARMITAGE

519 PEOPLE DIED WHILST AT
THEIR WORK DESKS THIS YEAR

RUSHIKA WICK

519 people died whilst at their work desks this year. The statistics reveal that employees who had been at the same workplace for more than ten years were ten times more likely to expire in this manner, and that more artists in their "day jobs" died than any other category of primary occupation. A team of scientists analysed the position of the bodies as found on the desks:

60% were reaching out for something in the moment, 21% were writing reports that appeared to be turning into poems and 10% had been trying to leave their desks. 9% had disappeared within the minute after death. In these cases, a very faint outline of the body in fine ochre dust and the scent of violets remained. The first person to pass away in this manner was writing a treatise called *Making a Fool of Death*, complete with woodblock illustrations from an unpublished eighteenth-century Hungarian occult manual. In this arresting work,

small men with elongated noses enter into discourse with winged mice. In a double-page spread, titled "Underworld of Labour", hundreds of bent figures sit below the floor of a wedding banquet, toiling over production of armour and weaponry, their beaded ribcages and perpetually hungry eyes gleaming in the pale light. At the bottom right of this picture women try to pass themselves off as men, betrayed by escaping breasts and grabbed at by other workers.

The last person to die in this manner within the financial year was a fine artist engaged as a paralegal in the City. The night before she died, she was working on a self-portrait in oils, wearing an exquisite floral coronet of cosmos and floating grass-heads (which remains unfinished).

The advice for concerned readers is to consider hot-desking and drink green tea, high in antioxidants. A relaxation app linked to this study is also available to purchase.

ZONA

TARQUIN LANDSEER

In the aftermath the land
became a source of bitterness.
The wormwood turned.
Black storks rose in a raucous cloud
above the dead red pines.

An eternal shadow cast,
the blood count dropped.
Iodine in their glands,
cows were still milked;
a yield wrong on the tongue.

The very grain of things jarred,
germ cells itched enough
to form a teras in the womb –
a slinked fleshy mass of mooncalf.

A gimcrack tomb was built
as if it might consume the corpse,
the elephant's foot at its core.

Among whispers of decay
the atomic pile stiffened with rust.
Winter chilled the heat
in the cold shutdown.

Aliened babushkas in headscarves,
some with goitred throats,
went out on a limb
to pick up sickeners.

Up against the elements
they hunted for dark puffballs,

bald heads amidst the carats of graphite
and fission fungus
where the ink caps dripped
damp in the rainout.

At the half-life mark of caesium
the stressors have long gone.
Wolves with whole skin
roam the amusement park,
back from the brink;
raccoon dogs raise a melancholy whine
by the crackling substation,

silvered swans dabble in the cooling ponds.
A sounder of swine trot by the smokery
and root about.
Crickets static-click like Geiger counters
in the livid grass at the tipping point.

CILLÍNÍ

CAROL CAFFREY

The pony and trap at midnight, darkness
covering the shame of day, they come to bury
the unshriven: the suicides, mentally ill,
infants, outcast mothers.

Around a sodden mound or hidden among brambles,
in cliff-crannies at the ocean's edge and under
cover of ancient ring forts – random
arrangements of stones disguise the places

where those outside the graveyard walls,
outside the grace of the Church,
lie unremarked, invisible on the map that history
has decreed, their footfalls lost forever.

What contamination did they fear,
those midnight riders, that they must banish
the innocents, pile babies between mothers' legs,
tandem burials, to become unremembered bones?

Draw back the night and call this ground that echoes
with their cries – sacred. Let the wind blow softly
through their names. Feather them down
into the grace of remembrance.

*Cillíní – Irish; unconsecrated burial grounds, usually
for unbaptised infants.*

BABY

LOUISA ARMITAGE

I did not hear a bang, just slowly fell
awake to spot my stomach's peachy swell.
Like creeping heat unheeded till a fire,
in shock, I heave a globe through murky mire.
My final grunt sees magma spray hot worms.
Listen. Leaden wait. First bleat. It squirms
and falls into an ignorant abyss.
I guess deep dread's a normal part of this.

A midwife steals the body, counts the toes.
"There's extra fingers. We'll get rid of those."
She hands me fists of bloody bandages,
clips that she's seeing more and more of this.
"Of what?" I ask, but cannot bear to hear,
distracted by a blistered ridge of ear.

Unwrapping swaddle like a foiled sweet,
my fingers find the skin is cracked like peat.
It's made of earth. Is something wrong?
Should skin crumble? The midwife's gone.
The head flops back, a glacial howl,
a wave of shit spurts from the bowel.
The genitals a mess – it's hard to tell
but from the weight, she feels female.

I trace her contours with intrepid thumbs
and feel saliva swirl around my tongue.
The baby looks divine. Is it remiss
to eat this treat? But wait, there's more to this:
a sacrilegious sack blooms at the crotch,
a penis arches like a snake. I watch
as iridescent arcs of urine soar,
mapping golden seas across the floor.
Then eyelids rise, it aims machine-gun sight

and plumes of want surge skywards, clouding light.
I'm billowing from every orifice.
All this disgorging leaves me ravenous.

I burn the soiled nappies, breathe them in,
mine snot, frack gas, ignore the rumbling.
Its shit grows sweeter, causes cavities.
My teeth begin to break but I still need
to slurp all that it has until I hurl,
sit back, lick lips, drink in my boyish girl.
And there's the whimper, spluttered, but too late.
It's sick, twig thin, the heartbeat featherweight.

I could have stopped, assessed and learnt to nurse.
My lips begin to crackle: "Rest now, hush.
You'll be OK, it's easy dying first.
A cloudburst of apologies, now shush."

NON-FICTION

THEY FUCK YOU UP
(BUT WHO ARE "THEY"?):
          INTERSECTIONALITY,
      CONFLICT AND CLIMATE

SEASON BUTLER

W hen I started scribbling the first notes that would eventually become my debut novel, *Cygnet*, a question was rumbling in literary and academic circles: Where – beyond Ian McEwan's *Solar* – was the mainstream literary fiction confronting the climate crisis directly? Of course, sci-fi, fantasy, young adult fiction and other more marginalised genres had long since taken up ecological consequences in the construction of dystopias. On the adult literary lists, *The Road* chilled readers with Cormac McCarthy's cruelly optimistic death march through a near-future landscape of abruptly arrested growth, a cautionary tale where hope itself acts as the antagonist. With *The Hungry Tide*, Amitav Ghosh gave his Global North audience a glimpse of life at the tempestuous front line of rising seas. In my own place and time, literary fiction seemed to reflect a belief that global heating was not here. At least not yet.

Given these observations about genre, temporalities and geographies, I wondered if readers like me, in the relative comfort of Europe, felt able to hold climate chaos in an abstract corner of our imaginations, infinitely deferrable into "someday, elsewhere" and affecting unfortunate "Others". Big questions around belonging, responsibility and empathy emerge as greater numbers of writers globally use fiction to address the climate emergency as something urgent, proximate and personal.

Amitav Ghosh's 2016 polemic *The Great Derangement* engages these questions in an eloquent, extended form, framing climate change as a crisis of imagination and, by extension, a crisis of culture.[1] By the time of *Cygnet*'s publication earlier this year, numerous writers across forms, genres and platforms had taken up the gauntlet and my novel joins the growing corpus of literature set against the anxiety and ennui of a present moment in the shadow of the looming, proliferating dog days on our horizon.

As the corpus changes, so do the questions we should demand from it. How do writers approach their word-work, as Toni Morrison calls it, which is also always world-making, while the world seems only able to wither, ignite, submerge? How do we write the pain, the fear, the regret, and maybe even the hope, with energy and clarity and love?

We might now begin interrogating how we write about this catastrophe, no longer simply a hazy hypothetical or potentially benign "change". The consciousness-raising agenda is long obsolete – we are convinced, or we are lying. Even this question of "how" misses the point, since there will be no unified or singular approach. When we write about life, love, adventure, family, work, travel – when we write about our world, our present – our prose will be steeped in methane and carbon, located at various proximities from some semblance of safety. As we reckon with fiction's old frenemies – time, place, the legacy of generations – we do so in a state of bewilderment, unreliability, betrayal and guilt.

And we won't find a single, simple through-line in how we write about the disaster at hand because of the profound differences in how its impacts are felt by our characters. While ecological movements once focused on the universality of environmental problems as challenges everyone would face, it is becoming clear that the impacts of this issue are as unequal as the economic systems under which they have been able to thrive. Xiuhtezcatl Martinez, musician and veteran climate activist since the age of six (he is now nineteen), observes the paradoxes and the attendant exacerbation of race and class antagonisms as the emergency, and our response to it, escalate:

> When I first started working in the climate movement in 2006, a lot of people saw the environment as a privileged thing to care about. Climate change and nature conservancy have been seen as primarily white issues. Part of this was a reflection of people empowered in leadership roles. I saw that marginalized communities were more likely to face income inequality and struggle to thrive in a system historically stacked against them. Issues like climate change didn't seem as important as the immediate challenges many of these communities faced.
>
> Climate change and fossil-fuel extraction disproportion-ately affect communities of color. We have traditionally viewed climate change as an issue separate from us. Images and videos of melting ice caps and polar bears weren't as relatable for inner-city communities prioritizing

immediate safety and survival. Many people of color were
excluded from the traditional environmental movement.[2]

Socio-economic and political differences gain magnitude on a
warming, stormy planet. The realities of life across colour lines,
below the poverty line, under glass ceilings of many kinds, all
raise the stakes, heightening the relevance of difference-conscious
approaches to character and plot. To create round characters (as
E. M. Forster called them) in an age when the consequences of
inequality are increasingly grave, the identity-matrix framework
offered by intersectionality is emerging as a useful tool in the
novelist's kit. Intersectional thinkers and practitioners are
currently celebrating the thirtieth anniversary of the term's
coinage by feminist legal theorist Kimberlé Crenshaw.[3] It focuses
our attention on the ways in which privilege and marginalisation
impact our life chances and inform the complexity of the conflicts
in our lives, urging nuanced understandings of difference while
also opening spaces for coalition and solidarity.

Cygnet's unnamed protagonist – let's call her The Kid – comes
of age as the twenty-first century is still in its teens, possessing the
intelligence, resourcefulness and wit typical (but not stereotypical)
of young, under-privileged Black girls in the United States. Before
the novel opens, The Kid has been taken in by her grandmother
after social services discovered her parents' drug problem. That
is how she finds herself on Swan Island, an old-age separatist
community ten miles off the coast of New Hampshire, a haven
from the dangers and degradation of growing old in a society
that valorises youth and discards anyone who's not valuable to
the system of neoliberal exploitation. She is told to hold tight and
wait, that her folks just need some time to clean up and get things
back to the precarious state of normality that, at times, they're
able to maintain. But when her grandmother dies, she isn't able
to contact her parents and has no choice but to remain, or else
leave and risk never seeing them again. Meanwhile, the island's
coast is eroding through a series of landslips, literally threatening
the ground beneath her, and the islanders – who proudly call
themselves Wrinklies – let her know that she has imposed on
their reluctant hospitality long enough.

At only seventeen, The Kid is weary of debt, crisis, emergency, but life just won't cut her a break. With an identity at the intersection of multiple, mutually reinforcing oppressed identities in terms of race, gender, class and age, she is at the sharp end of a catastrophe already unfolding in the Global South and marginalised communities in the Global North. Her house is falling down, polluted seas are rising, time is running out.

On our own little island nation, rebellion is in the air, on the streets, in ripped jeans and yellow vests, costumed and plain-clothed. Change-any-change rebellion, single-issue rebellion, it's-all-connected rebellion, please-don't-leave rebellion, not-in-my-backyard rebellion. Old certainties have grown defiant. Around the world, fires erupt out of season, pushing against the efforts of volunteers and the coerced alike to keep them at bay.[4] In the USA, the wealthy go private: Kim and Kanye reportedly used a bought-in private fire service to protect their home while the property of the less rich, the middle class, the disposable classes, charred like something out of Sarah Connor's worst nightmare.[5]

I had never even heard of a private fire service before, and of all the things that frighten me about the moment we're living through, this detail has gotten under my skin like a particularly malignant tick. It really shouldn't surprise me; I was born in the US, in the Reagan-Thatcher world, with normalised private health care and private property worth killing and dying for, so why wouldn't the privatisation of survival emerge as the endgame of neoliberalism?

And, of course, what I feel isn't surprise at all. It's fear. The fear that comes with seeing that old walls are being fortified, and new walls are going up, and I am, and always have been, on the wrong side of them.

The good news? I'm not alone. Not by a long shot. Like The Kid, I've existed for some time at the intersection of multiple, mutually reinforcing identities in terms of race, gender, class, (dis)ability. (And someday, sooner than I imagine, I'll emerge from the relative privilege of middle age back into marginalised age, but instead of the marginalisation of youth it will be the marginalisation of my dotage.) At this intersection, I am in good company.

The rebellion is calling time, disrupting the operation of a parasitic system. Under all the slogans from all the sides of all the arguments is a simple demand, with a similar ring to babies crying. I don't mean infantile; I mean unadulterated truth. Give me what I need and keep me far from that which kills me. We demand survival.

The generation currently coming of age are showing themselves as more than the poster children of centrist politics, symbols of the innocents who as Lee Edelman asserts, are claimed by every side of mainstream politics as the cause for which power advances its agenda.[6] They are agents of their own survival, fledgling authors of a livable future. They are not waiting for a poisoned inheritance. Across the world, young people are abandoning their classrooms to protest government inaction and demand climate justice. They are wielding their identities to force system change. School strikes look primed to give way to general strikes.

For sociologists Patricia Hill Collins and Sirma Bilge, this is only apt. In their 2016 overview, *Intersectionality*, Collins and Bilge note that young people "are often among the first interconnections among systems of power that put them at risk". Their naturalised lack of political power grants them a perspective on "age as a system of power firsthand":

> [C]hildren, teenagers, and young adults have a special vantage point on intersecting social inequalities of ethnicity, religion, gender, sexuality, and race. They know that their neighborhoods receive inferior services and special policing. They see that their schools have less experienced teachers, old and dilapidated buildings, and outdated textbooks. They know that jobs for teenagers are minimal, and that the legitimate jobs that do exist pay little and have few benefits. Race, class, gender, and citizenship categories disadvantage many groups under neoliberal policies, yet, because age straddles all of these categories, young people's experiences of social problems are intensified.[7]

These protestors, many of whom are well below voting age, are increasingly occupying democracy's underused spaces – the streets, the commons and quotidian infrastructure – and leveraging what few assets they possess to demand meaningful action.

From some vantage points, this looks like a fightback by the young against the old, framed within narratives of intergenerational exploitation and conflict. Old people bought all the houses and now it takes two jobs just to make rent. Old people burned oil like there was no tomorrow and now there will be no tomorrow. Old people voted Leave. Philip Larkin's often quoted observation, "They fuck you up, your mum and dad", seems true beyond the individual neuroses; now our folks' toxic choices affect our infrastructure, our agriculture, even our weather. We can't breathe; we can't drink the water; we can't stay here much longer.

According to the charity Age UK, "1.9 million pensioners (16 per cent) are living in relative poverty [...] 29 per cent of Asian or Asian British pensioners and 33 per cent of Black or Black British, compared to 14 per cent of white pensioners." One in seven pensioners live in "care deserts", amounting to over one million people lacking the care they need after a decade of the current ruling party's austerity policies. A troubling number of elderly Britons would struggle to meet an unexpected £200 expense.[8]

So many of the values of extraction and exploitation that caused the climate crisis make old age a time of almost unthinkable precarity and marginalisation. As Simone de Beauvoir observed fifty years ago: "The economy is founded upon profit. The human working stock is of interest only in so far as it is profitable. When it is no longer profitable it is tossed aside."[9]

Like other marginalised people, as an identity group the elderly face near-constant stereotyping and overdetermination. To suggest that someone is old almost always constitutes an insult, and polite people will engage in the most absurd verbal gymnastics to avoid this. Evasion, omission and passing are common. Older people who have not accumulated capital in the form of home ownership, those whose pensions have been depleted by market fluctuations or those whose age diminishes their desirability to prospective employers, often find themselves in extremely precarious positions. As the population lives longer on average, this precarity can last for decades. In line with other forms of social marginalisation, the oppression of older people appears extremely durable; the naturalisation of social narratives of ageing contributes to this durability.

To regard climate change as essentially a situation wherein the actions of the old have diminished the life chances of the young is to allow many of the real causal agents and beneficiaries of the climate crisis to remain concealed from view. It's a straw man that keeps us from recognising our shared interests, across our differences.

Intersectionality is an analytical framework which recognises the various aspects of our identities that are socially determined – race, gender, class, (dis)ability, sexuality, you get the picture – as simultaneous and mutually informing. Writers, thinkers and campaigners such as the Combahee River Collective, Audre Lorde, Angela Davis and Gloria Anzaldúa all grounded their work in the ways in which feminist politics need to recognise that the demands and challenges facing women vary as gender intersects with other identity subject positions such as race.

Intersectionality has traditionally placed a specific focus on marginalised groups, and the catastrophic impact of climate instability will continue to be felt first and most profoundly by those on the social, political and geographical margins. Naomi Klein's landmark treatise on the climate emergency, *This Changes Everything*, highlights the ways that global warming doubles-down on the ongoing legacy of white settler colonialism and contemporary systems of oppression, a phenomenon known as environmental racism:

> Running an economy on energy sources that release poisons as an unavoidable part of their extraction and refining has always required sacrifice zones – whole subsets of humanity categorized as less than fully human, which made their poisoning in the name of progress somehow acceptable.
>
> And for a very long time, sacrifice zones all shared a few elements in common. They were poor places. Out-of-the-way places. Places where residents lacked political power, usually having to do with some combination of race,

language, and class. And the people who lived in these condemned places knew they had been written off. [...]

Through various feats of denialism and racism, it was possible for privileged people in North America and Europe to mentally cordon off these unlucky places as hinterlands, wastelands, nowheres [...]

And up until quite recently, that has held up as the grand bargain of the carbon age: the people reaping the bulk of the benefits of extractivism pretend not to see the costs of that comfort so long as the sacrifice zones are kept safely out of view.[10]

Even as the "trickle up" immiseration of climate crisis begins to trouble the white, the middle class, the Global North, Klein is careful to remind us that, "[n]one of this means that environmental impacts are suddenly evenly distributed. Historically marginalized people in the Global South, as well as communities of color in the Global North, are still at far greater risk of living downstream from a mine, next door to a refinery, or next to a pipeline, just as they are more vulnerable to the impacts of climate change."[11]

One of William Gibson's famous aphorisms, "The future is already here – it's just not very evenly distributed," usually referred to the benefits of the then burgeoning digital age.[12] Ironically, Gibson's maxim is equally true with regard to biosphere collapse and other effects of extractive capitalism; extreme weather, crop failure, famine, wars for control of scarce resources and a return to barbarous practices like public slave auctions are dystopian future scenarios for those of us in the Global North, consuming images of the present-tense dystopia visited in real time on those in the Global South.

Cygnet is set in a time of global ecological crisis, on social, political and geographical margins. The title alludes to *The Ugly Duckling*; it is a story of someone whose fundamental difference forecloses the possibility of belonging. To heighten the stakes for the protagonist, I chose to define this society by its hard-line exclusion of people with The Kid's defining characteristic: youth. Creating a space that was not just a retirement community but a *separatist* community generates a predominant antagonism

based on identity politics in order to explore how structures
of exclusion and belonging operate. My readers will be more
familiar with these structures through racism, misogyny,
xenophobia, homophobia, class bias, etc. By positioning a
marginalised identity as the normative one in the novel, *Cygnet*
further considers the implications of being an interloper in a
marginalised community's protected space, problematising
notions of entitlement to space and separatist strategies within
the wider discourse of identity politics.

Most of the identity subject positions that concern
intersectional thinkers operate on a binary, with the privileged
position at one side and the marginalised or oppressed position
at the other. Age is unique in this respect; as a social construct,
age looks more like a bell-shaped curve. We have very little
agency at the beginning of life. This increases as we enter the age
of majority, a normative life stage when we are granted certain
citizenship rights. As we approach old age, visibility and social
capital diminish. Therefore, with regard to age, the normative
subject position is situated in the middle of a curve rather than at
one end of a binary.

This bell-shaped progression through life means that the move
from a normative subject position into a marginal one is almost
certain. Age is unique in that almost everyone will eventually
experience a loss of privilege and depletion of social capital –
a potentially exponential loss for those already marginalised by
race, gender, class, sexuality, (dis)ability, etc. – in a move that is
so tied to biological temporal processes as to make the negativity
we too often ascribe to elderliness appear "natural". We will either
face an "early" death, or be rendered abject, Other, by old age.

Through separatist politics, the Swans have found a way to
embrace their own abjection. Calling themselves "Wrinklies",
they happily eschew the notion that ageing "successfully" means
appearing not to age at all. They are the kind of old people who,
"rejected by society," de Beauvoir observes, "find that the rejection
works in their favour, since they no longer have to trouble about
pleasing. In them we see that indifference to public opinion which
Aristotle called 'shamelessness' and which is the beginning of
freedom. [...] They no longer defined themselves by their social

function: they felt themselves to be individuals, with the power to decide upon their conduct not according to accepted ideas but according to their own wishes."[13] They age their own way, they let things wear out, they create support systems to keep themselves and each other fed on home-grown crops, high on home-grown crops, partying until last orders, receptive to what comes next.

In *Cygnet* I used E. M. Forster's notion of "roundness" in characters as a way of counteracting the flattening effects of stereotyping.[14] Forster's round characters have physicality, psychology and history; all of these are inflected by race, as well as gender, class, sexuality and the rest. My notion of "intersectional roundness" endows characters – not necessarily every character, as per Forster's theorisation, which doesn't privilege roundness over flatness per se – with physicality, psychology and politics. Intersectional roundness makes difference – especially difference informed by power relations – a visible and productive element in character and plot. I think that intersectionality can be as valuable a tool for the writer as it is for the sociologist, activist or legal theorist.

Toni Morrison has written about her interest in "evaluat[ing] Black literature on what the writer does with the presence of an ancestor."[15] Within ambivalent relations across three generations and problematic relationships with history, the ideological and material legacy bequeathed by ancestor figures generates the impasse that The Kid must overcome in order to emerge. What is passed down through her parents and grandmother overdetermines and undermines her life chances. Casual drug use over the course of the novel suggests an unconscious mirroring of her parents' addictive behaviour as well as an addict's particular sense of queer time, one of Judith Halberstam's "pathologized modes of living that show little or no concern for longevity".[16] Betraying her lack of faith in a normative future, The Kid's aspirations through the novel rarely go beyond the bare means of survival. Her inheritance of her grandmother's house serves not as an asset and safe haven but as a financial burden because the mortgage (literally, "death pledge") must be paid by The Kid. For her, a house is a site of precarity, echoing the change in literal and symbolic value of home ownership after the 2007 subprime mortgage crisis. Historical ancestors appear in the vestiges of slavery that continue to limit the life chances of African Americans, survival strategies such as the oral transmission of folk knowledge and in the novel's concern with immobilisation and escape.

Apocalyptic situations in non-realistic spatio-temporal settings (the future, outer space, dystopias, etc.) suggest speculative fiction as a genre. Increasingly, however, climate change has brought an End Times narrative into the quotidian experience, subverting our generic expectations that fiction dealing with apocalypse will be futuristic. As the protagonist enters adulthood, the idea of a meaningful future is in doubt for an entire generation as climate forecasts suggest that an average temperature rise of over two degrees is almost certain.

The Kid's emergence into adulthood and historical time within a realistic frame of everyday time and a verifiable contemporary moment can evoke a sense of dissonance with the looming presence of an end-of-days catastrophe, complicating the perception of my novel as realist or speculative fiction. Specific software and uses of technology (hacking manoeuvres, editing software) will date the novel, and several characters' dates of birth are mentioned; an interested reader can calculate the novel's setting in the recent past. Still, many of my early readers perceived the novel as set in the near future. This is the kind of temporal paradox that I feel is appropriate to the climate change novel. I hope that through the empathetic connection between the reader and the protagonist, I can facilitate an experience of climate change that is immediate, urgent and proximal while also staggering in scale.

Contemporary fiction has the potential to explore strategies for managing the work of life-making at a moment when it is more likely than ever that the world as we know it is coming to an end. It is an apocalypse on the scale that would assign it to speculative fiction but which the real world has caught up with, so to speak, opening new relationships to space and time, the historical and the contemporary, inheritance and legacy. How we invest materially and affectively in the future, and our ability to cope with the outcomes of past investments, are all at stake on a warming planet. Identity informs the lived experience of the historical present in the immediacy and materiality of our defining existential threat.

The Kid's parents, still very much in the grip of addiction, live in what William S. Burroughs called Junk Time, and also Judith Halberstam's queer time, inasmuch as normative stability and longevity – for better or worse – are not their primary driver.[17] The Wrinklies' relationship to time is queered too, by their rejection of the society that defines them as expired. De Beauvoir again: "Age changes our relationship with time: as the years go by our future shortens, while our past grows heavier."[18] The Kid finds affinity with this, as the real-life End Times approach, sidling right up to her door. She has the burden of the future, which "spreads out in front of her like an ocean of days". At the same time, she carries a deeply troubled past of trauma and neglect, a burden that fatigues her, making her feel much older than she is. In this strange society which rejects many of the conventions of a normative timeline, and existing at the intersection of marginalised race, gender and class, The Kid's experience of time and space is constantly unsettled. This disorientation, this wily, unreliable relationship to the mundane ticks of time and the once solid ground beneath our feet, is something I think more and more of us will relate to as the crisis, and the resistance, continue to unfold.

In 1962, at the age of fifty-five, Rachel Carson published her classic text *Silent Spring*. In prose seasoned with chemistry, reportage, mythology and fable, the rich narrative diversity in its form underpins her warnings about loss of biodiversity. Stories matter. Our minds are not easily given to monoculture. Our understanding does not live on fact or fiction alone.

The dominant, ecocidal narrative will continue to try to discredit the resistance. The mouthpieces of the carbon-hungry elite love to trot out ad hominem attacks to render sensible policies cartoonish with foppish straw-man argumentation. The idea is that if you have a carbon footprint, *you* can't tell *me* to change anything. To advance any argument, you must be answerable to impossible moral standards. Only absolute innocence will suffice. These ad hominem attempts at misdirection have started to appear directed towards Greta Thunberg, with wannabe-bad-boy mega-toff Toby Young's pitiful jab at her supposed "privileged" background (Young's own use of his privilege makes his comments barely worth the exertion of rolling your eyes); *Spiked* editor Brendan O'Neill disingenuously claims to read sinister undertones in Thunberg's delivery of her speeches to parliaments, forums and crowds of activists, an oratory style that seems to me evidence of refreshing gravitas and lucidity.[19] Maybe, despite the baby face, she is woman enough to be called crazy for speaking sense in a public forum.

Those who came before us knew well the value of collaboration across identity lines. Black Panther Fred Hampton saw the shared struggles in emancipatory movements of poor whites in Appalachia, Puerto Ricans in Chicago, and facilitated coalitions against their shared enemy – namely, capitalist exploitation. Toni Morrison's Nobel speech narrates a conversation between young and old, extending a story of understanding between the margins, across the chasm between youth and age.[20] And we see this in the imperfect diversity of the boots on the ground demanding system change to keep us all alive. Isra Hirsi, Xiuhtezcatl Martinez, Greta Thunberg and their peers are building on the foundations laid by the *Silent Spring* generation, fighting with them, refusing to have their identities instrumentalised by the narratives of those who manufacture our fear, our precarity, our hunger for profit.

Martinez connects with his ancestors in his activist work. Thunberg concludes her TED talk with a projection of herself as a grandmother.[21] These imaginative gestures encourage us to think of ourselves as part of a continuum, to remember that, wherever we fall on the intersectional matrix, we're the beneficiaries of radical movements every time we vote, enjoy a weekend off or make empowered decisions about our own health. And we can imagine ourselves as ancestors our successors can be proud of. Age is the future for us all. If we're not swans, we're cygnets. We all stand to inherit the world we're making now.

1   Amitav Ghosh, *The Great Derangement: Climate Change and the Unthinkable* (Chicago: University of Chicago Press, 2016).
2   Xiuhtezcatl Martinez, *We Rise: The Earth Guardians Guide to Building a Movement that Restores the Planet* (Emmaus: Rodale Books, 2017), 190.
3   Kimberlé Crenshaw, "Demarginalizing the Intersection of Race and Sex: A Black Feminist Critique of Antidiscrimination Doctrine, Feminist Theory and Antiracist Politics", *University of Chicago Legal Forum*, 1989/1, 139–167.

4   German Lopez, "California is using prison labor to fight its record wildfires",
        Vox (9 August 2018). <https://www.vox.com/2018/8/9/17670494/california-
        prison-labor-mendocino-carr-ferguson-wildfires> accessed 1 April, 2019.

5   Alexis C. Madrigal, "Kim Kardashian's Private Firefighters Expose
        America's Fault Lines", *The Atlantic* (14 November 2018). <https://www.
        theatlantic.com/technology/archive/2018/11/kim-kardashian-kanye-west-
        history-private-firefighting/575887/> accessed 1 April, 2019.

6   Lee Edelman, *No Future: Queer Theory and the Death Drive* (Durham:
        Duke University Press, 2004).

7   Patricia Hill Collins and Sirma Bilge, *Intersectionality* (Cambridge: Polity
        Press, 2016), 117.

8   Age UK, "Poverty in later life" (April 2018). <https://www.ageuk.org.
        uk/globalassets/age-uk/documents/reports-and-publications/reports-and-
        briefings/money-matters/rb_apr18_poverty_in_later_life> accessed 1 April
        2019. "'Care deserts' mean older people aren't getting the care they need"
        (15 May 2019). <https://www.ageuk.org.uk/discover/2019/may/care-desert/>
        accessed 1 April 2019.

9   Simone de Beauvoir, *The Coming of Age* (New York: G. P. Putman's Sons,
        1972), 6.

10   Naomi Klein, *This Changes Everything: Capitalism vs. the Climate* (London:
        Penguin, 2014), 310–311.

11   Klein, 314.

12   There are various recorded instances of William Gibson offering this maxim,
        with slightly different wording, in media interviews and documentaries. See, for
        example, *Cyberpunk*, dir. by Marianne Trench (Intercon Productions, 1990)
        online film recording, YouTube, 17 July 2016 <https://www.youtube.com/
        watch?v=hRwU9zJcT60> accessed 16 June 2019; Brooke Gladstone, "The
        Science in Science Fiction," *Talk of the Nation*, NPR, 30 November 1999
        <https://www.npr.org/2018/10/22/1067220/the-science-in-science-fiction>
        accessed 19 June 2019.

13   de Beauvoir, 488.

14   E. M. Forster, "People" in *Aspects of the Novel* (London: Penguin, 2005).

15   Toni Morrison, *What Moves at the Margin: Selected Nonfiction*, Carolyn C.
        Denard, ed. (Jackson: University Press of Mississippi, 2008), 61.

16   Judith Halberstam, *In a Queer Time and Place: Transgender Bodies,
        Subcultural Lives* (New York: New York University Press, 2005), 152.

17   William S. Burroughs, *Junky: The Definitive Text of "Junk"* (London:
        Penguin, 1977 [2008]); Halberstam, *In a Queer Time and Place.*

18   de Beauvoir, 361.

19   Lowenna Waters, "Toby Young tried to troll Greta Thunberg for a second
        time, and it backfired again", in *The Independent* (24 April 2019) <https://
        www.indy100.com/article/toby-young-greta-thunberg-mother-eurovision-
        song-contest-malena-ernman-twitter-8884321> accessed 29 April 2019;
        Brendan O'Neill, "The cult of Greta Thunberg", in *Spiked* (22 April 2019)
        <https://www.spiked-online.com/2019/04/22/the-cult-of-greta-thunberg/>
        accessed 29 April 2019.

20   Toni Morrison, "Nobel Lecture," 7 December 1993. <https://www.nobelprize.
        org/prizes/literature/1993/morrison/lecture/> accessed 5 April 2019.

21   Greta Thunberg, "The disarming case to act right now on climate change"
        [video file] (November 2018). <https://www.ted.com/talks/greta_thunberg_
        the_disarming_case_to_act_right_now_on_climate?language=en> accessed
        1 April 2019.

FICTION

VISITOR NOTES:
ACACIA LODGE

DAVE WAKELY

Last updated: August 2151

INTRODUCTION

B uilt in 2014, Acacia Lodge offers a rare insight into domestic life in the early twenty-first century, a period of history we now refer to as the Age of Excess. Since 2147, experts from the Secular Millennium Council's Heritage Education Trust have worked to restore or preserve as much of the property and its contents as possible while respecting current legislation and health directives. Although many substantially older domestic properties remain, having proved easier to renovate and adapt to today's circumstances, few buildings from this era have survived and none is as well maintained.

The house owes its survival to the ruin of similar properties that once surrounded it, destroyed in repeated flash-flooding episodes during the 2040s. A historical local map is displayed on the mainland bank. Hidden behind an encircling stand of large coniferous trees (a species called Leylandii: x *Cuprocyparis leylandii*, or "Leyland cypress"), the house lay forgotten for over a hundred years on what had become an island, until it was discovered by two children who had made a raft to forage – unsuccessfully – for fruits and berries.

Acacia Lodge was purchased as a newly built property by Max and Alice Ernest the year before the birth of their first child, Sally. At the time of construction, it formed part of a "housing estate" – an area nearly a mile across containing several hundred domestic dwellings, arranged along arterial roads and branching dead ends. (Pre-dating the Language Purity Instructions, the latter were known by the French phrase *cul de sac*.)

Until the mid twenty-first century, people lived mostly in individual dwellings of various sizes, shared only with immediate relatives or intimates. Today's communal living arrangements were unusual outside urban areas, where so-called Homes in Multiple Occupation (HIMOs) were considered a social problem. Shared housing was usually adopted through personal preference, due to either religious or political beliefs, or by those on low incomes. Before the later emigrations and repatriations, some non-indigenous populations with a cultural practice of "extended family living" lived in larger groupings, especially those from Southern Asia; their number was far greater than today.

It is one of the many ironies around Acacia Lodge that we know less about its history and inhabitants than about many earlier properties. Record-keeping in the early twenty-first century was mostly undertaken by electronic means and, unlike the extensive paper records kept in previous eras, much of this material is now lost. As we shall see, however, the activities of certain family members meant that some of their actions were documented by others; these external sources have proved invaluable to our understanding.

THE APPROACH

Acacia Lodge is approached via a recently constructed footbridge (made by Trust volunteers from local sustainable materials) over what is now a surrounding dry ditch some eight feet wide and fifteen feet deep. Rusted winch mechanisms on the island bank suggest that access was controlled at some point by a drawbridge. For visitor safety, large quantities of barbed wire and broken glass, presumably added to repel unwelcome visitors, have been dredged from the moat.

Note: To present the house authentically, thick external metal shutters have been removed from the windows and doors. A surviving diary shows these defensive structures were added shortly before the house was abandoned. A heavily scarred window shield can be seen at the end of the tour.

As you face the house, the small area of scrubland directly ahead would have been a "front garden". While this appears horticultural, the plants were mostly ornamental, with the exception of fruit trees (grown as much for their blossom) and a small number of herbs. Botanists have discovered rosemary, bay laurel and thyme, which would have been used in domestic cooking rather than for medicinal purposes, along with traces of many species that would not survive our modern hot, wet summers. The large Leylandii have been removed to enable restoration, together with other then commonly grown but highly toxic plants such as hydrangea [*Hydrangea macrophylla*], azalea [*Rhododendron degronianum*] and laburnum [*Laburnum anagyroides*].

On the left-hand side of the property, you will see a strip of land surfaced with bitumen and stone chippings that leads to a vertically opening metal doorway. This would have been used to park a private motor car and to access the house's integral garage. A badly decayed car, manufactured in what was then South Korea, was discovered here and is undergoing off-site restoration. Intended to protect vehicles from the elements, garages were frequently used as large cupboards for domestic storage, despite the deterioration caused to vehicles left in the open air for long periods. At the end of your tour, you will visit the garage and see how it was later repurposed.

Acacia Lodge's fate at the hands of the climate is a rare example of "natural thinning": the organic lowering of the density of buildings to support crop-growing and livestock husbandry. In most areas, thinning has been enforced to allow communities to support themselves healthily. Many surviving multi-storey buildings, often now designated as community workshops, would have been domestic apartments without any outside space. Allotments existed but were far from universal; few people relied on them for sustenance or barter.

Safety Note: On entering, please wear your face mask at all times and ensure your cotton overclothes and shoes are properly fitted. Do not handle any items within the property unless explicitly instructed by your Tour Guide: many include materials that are no longer available or are prohibited for legal or technical reasons. While any objects known to be hazardous are clearly labelled, some microbes may have survived that can cause currently untreatable medical conditions.

PORCH AND ENTRANCE HALL

While all approved dwellings now have an enclosed doorway area for decontamination and the donning or shedding of outdoor wear, porches were typically present in this era only in the houses of the "middle classes", a socio-economic grouping referred to by one prime minister of the period – without ironic intent – as JAMs (those "just about managing"). Property size was an indicator of wealth: before the introduction of Basic Income, home ownership was a vehicle for personal investment. Even large properties often contained only one or two adults, since families rarely moved to smaller properties as they reduced in number. Homelessness was a growing social problem.

On the left, you can see a coat rack carved from mahogany, a non-native tree that could then still be imported. You will see innumerable objects of foreign origin throughout the house: these would have been regarded as signs not of disloyalty but of a sophisticated and cosmopolitan outlook.

One of the house's most overlooked items hangs on the wall on your right, next to a large wooden barometer. Made in the style of a Victorian needlework sampler, although dated 2019, there is a framed quotation: "Have nothing in your houses that you do not know to be useful, or believe to be beautiful." The words come from a lecture delivered in 1880 by William Morris, a wealthy Victorian manufacturer of expensive domestic furnishings who was also a campaigning socialist.

The critical word here is "or". Acacia Lodge dates from the final years of a period marked by excessive consumption and frivolous concerns, not least fashion; utility was not an unknown concept, but was rarely given much consideration. Notice, for example, the thick blue carpeting that extends throughout the house despite the long-lasting hard flooring below. It is woven from acrylic, a now prohibited man-made fibre that was favoured at the time for its durability and relative low cost. Pricing was determined by the need to generate profit at each stage of manufacture and distribution; environmental impact was a concern for only a subset of domestic items and behaviours, and the Ernests' carpet choice would not have been subject to either enforced penalties or social stigma.

THE KITCHEN

Although contemporary households have reverted to earlier domestic models, with cooking and eating undertaken as communal activities within a shared living space, the kitchen is typical of the early twenty-first century. There is no open fire, as heating was supplied separately. Instead, you can see a range of metal items, all painted white. Kitchen appliances were often referred to as "white goods", although they were used by people of all skin colours who could afford them.

Neither is there a larder, as these were considered old-fashioned. Storage cupboards contained a wide selection of tinned goods, items used predominantly to augment or garnish meals rather than to provide their basic components. Few people ate seasonally, and food would have been gathered intermittently rather than daily, with domestic refrigerators keeping items at artificially low temperatures for long periods. As well as reducing nutritional value, this consumed considerable amounts of electricity: judging by surviving weather records, far more than that generated by the property's roof-mounted solar panels.

The house was abandoned before the Fracking Disaster of 2048 and the subsequent restrictions on private electricity use. Acacia Lodge also had electrically powered apparatus for the washing and drying of clothing; while these saved physical labour, they consumed large quantities of water and accelerated the deterioration of clothing.

Cooking was performed using a stove that combined a gas-powered hob and grill with an electrically powered oven, or in a now obsolete device called a microwave. This metal box cooked food by irradiating it; a century after the Sizewell Incident, this process seems as bizarre as the earlier use of powdered lead as a skin enhancer. (See also later notes on the Garden.)

To the left of the large table, able to seat eight people though used mainly as a food-preparation surface, you can see a row of coloured containers used to sort household waste into categories that included food scraps, paper and glass, and – in the largest – non-recyclable items. These were collected, usually full, on a weekly basis. Almost a third of all purchased food was thrown away; this figure was higher for fruit and vegetables, many of which were imported. There was no garden compost heap, nor any record of a local communal facility. (Note also that the containers themselves are made from non-biodegradable plastics.)

In addition, households disposed of large quantities of needless packaging, both paper and plastic. Packaging's primary purpose was not protection, of either goods or consumers, but the promotion of consumption. Often heavily printed with manufacturers' identification marks and idealised imagery, only a small percentage of the surface area listed nutritional value or suggested secondary usage.

THE STUDY

Originally a second reception room, this smaller downstairs room was used as a workspace. Max Ernest was an insurance salesman; like most adults, he would have travelled some distance to an office. Records show that he commuted forty miles a day until the business collapsed and then took local work as a private security guard, a popular form of employment as social disturbance increased.

Alice Ernest worked in education as a mindfulness lecturer. While this has been a core curriculum subject since formal education was re-established, learning materials found here bear no relation to today's Citizen Conduct Manual. Topic lists reflect a focus on the individual, with a desire to avoid negative emotions towards the self rather than developing concern for and cooperation with others. A part-time employee at the local university until its abolition in 2038, Alice also had private clients, typically female and wealthy, and a folder of invoices shows that she charged a very high hourly rate. (Unusually for this period, she earned considerably more than her husband.) Typical of their time in many of their behaviours, the Ernests were also "progressives" and would have been subject to increasing social suspicion.

Like most of the rooms, the study contains the era's ubiquitous device: a computer. Connected to the Internet (now available only to senior Global Security Council staff), computers were used not only to store information, but for correspondence, shopping, research and entertainment. Many traditional media – books, audio, video – were "digitised" to enable them to be used on computers and mobile handheld devices. Even though this brought advantages in portable access, the fall of the major Internet service companies after the Final Personal Data Crisis of 2037 meant that a vast quantity of material was lost.

This room contains the highest number of handmade artefacts, although whether they are – to cite the framed William Morris quotation you saw in the entrance hall – useful or beautiful is debatable. Engravings on the bases of the clumsily decorated and poorly constructed vase-like objects (none of which is watertight) reveal that they were personal gifts from Alice's students: a Pottery for Self-Expression Workshop leaflet was found among her papers. Despite the availability of practical craft-skills courses, most people's crafting abilities and knowledge of materials were far below the standards of today's Craft Guild Apprenticeship schemes. From her papers, Alice's handwriting was also poor: teaching of this vital competence had been abandoned, reflecting the predominant use of keyboards rather than pens or pencils.

THE LIVING ROOM

Occupying the back half of the ground floor, this room's lavish use of space is striking: it could accommodate the entire family twice over. But although the two sofas and accompanying armchairs suggest a communal space, this was true more in capacity than in everyday use. Principal carpet wear shows paths from the hallway to the floor-length external windows, which originally opened onto a conservatory, and to one sofa that shows heavier use. It's likely that this room was mainly used by only one or two people, and that they were mostly sedentary.

Although the distinction would have been less sharp than fifty years earlier, this era still saw a fundamental difference between "work" and "leisure": those in paid employment worked increasingly long hours and use of networked computers blurred divisions between home and workplace. Patterns of leisure were also very different. Notice how the enormous, long-defunct television set is the focus of attention here. In 2030, over a thousand broadcast channels were available. A handful were dedicated to news, sports or the arts, but most provided low-grade entertainment; the medium's educational potential was vastly underexploited. Musical instruments, common in earlier eras, are notably absent here: entertainment was considered something to be paid for and absorbed passively, rather than as a pastime that encouraged active participation.

The shelving unit contains numerous ornamental objects, and the nearby framed photograph montage suggests that these are souvenirs of foreign travel: images show family members in European or tropical locations. (As you will see later, some photographs have been moved to other rooms.) Travel outside the country – mostly by aeroplane – was unrestricted. Commercial travel companies operated freely and tourism was a major industry, despite rising civil unrest in some popular destinations. Although a Portuguese phrase book was found in the house, travel was rarely undertaken for any educational purpose.

Note also that each item of furniture serves only one purpose. None of the chairs, for example, uses the area below the seat as storage. The one exception is the large black lacquered chest in the centre of the room, identified as Indonesian. Its lid – badly damaged by hot-beverage vessels, as tea and coffee would have been consumed in preference to water – is inlaid with the shells of several now extinct marine species.

When opened, the contents were a surprise for anthropologists: initially hard to identify, tooth marks in their surfaces showed that these were "dog toys". Dogs and cats were commonly kept as "pets". Treated as additional family members, these animals made no contribution to human diet or labours. As well as evidence of dog hairs throughout the carpeting, two canine skeletons were unearthed in the rear garden, along with the bones of a rodent, thought to have been a hamster. There are no indications that the Ernests kept any other, more practical livestock.

THE GARDEN

Through the rear windows of the living room, you can see an area of broken paving where the conservatory once stood. This was a status symbol: expensive to build, its glass construction would also have made it costly to heat during the bitterly cold winters of the 2040s. (Its inherent lack of external security may have led to its removal, which would also have aided the attachment of the external grilles.) Unlike the orangeries of earlier periods, conservatories were used as additional leisure areas rather than to grow tender fruits and vegetables. A photograph in the living room shows Alice in a sleeveless summer dress, a baby in her lap, sitting here in a bamboo and wicker chair; bamboo – the most sustainable of all the materials evidenced in Acacia Lodge – had also been used to create the window blinds visible behind her.

In what remains of the original rear garden after catastrophic subsidence, you can see the remnants of a brick structure used as a barbecue area for outdoor cooking. Older visitors will be familiar with these from their stays in Civic Education Camps, although the Ernests' barbecue would have been used only with invited guests: its purpose was socialising, not socialisation. Excavation of the garden beyond has shown evidence only of strawberries (grown in very small quantities), barberries and Japanese quince; uncommon during the period, the fruits of the latter were probably never eaten.

THE MASTER BEDROOM

Despite the name – which was common contemporary usage – both Max and Alice would have slept here. Significantly larger than the other bedrooms, it has its own washing area consisting of a shower, hand basin and toilet, accessed by the door to the left of the bed. There was no composting of human waste or collection of used water. Even if the environmental impulse had registered, this would have been impractical as most toiletries contained high levels of chemical compounds.

The unbroken row of doors on the long left-hand wall conceals built-in wardrobes. The number of coat hangers found here suggests this would have been largely filled. Many garments survived, although it is notable that Alice's clothes were in several different sizes. Average calorie consumption was twice today's level and a lack of physical labour meant obesity was a widespread problem. The collection of "diet books" in the kitchen implies that at least some members of the family made attempts – presumably unsuccessful – to manage their weight.

For such a personal space, remarkably few truly personal objects were found in the room, although some may have been removed when the family abandoned the property. As elsewhere, there are a number of mass-produced items – mirrors, hairbrushes and the like – along with a copious accumulation of cosmetics. Artificial self-beautification was almost universal among women, and male vanity was also widespread: particularly striking is the number of pots of "anti-ageing creams", despite the lack of evidence of their effectiveness. This was an era of sexual competitiveness – divorces and extra-marital affairs were unexceptional – and maximising one's appearance was paramount.

This attitude to personal relationships was further evidenced in the contents of the bedside cabinets, where various "marital aids" – including several dildos and a cock ring – were found along with miscellaneous contraceptive devices. While declining male fertility means that contraception is now rarely an issue, many women in this era used an oral contraceptive widely referred to as "the Pill", despite evidence of medical harm and environmental impact. Before composting toilets, most waste was filtered into rivers; hermaphrodite fish were frequently found, damaged by waterborne hormones. Sexual satisfaction was judged largely on the basis of technical performance rather than on emotional comfort or demonstrativeness. This may also account for the large mirror on the ceiling above the bed: given the placement of light fittings, it is doubtful that it was intended to reflect illumination.

"SALLY'S ROOM"

The nameplate is misleading, as there is no evidence that the Ernests' daughter lived in the house after the age of eighteen. Entering the room immediately shows that its final tenant was someone very different. We know from hospital archives that this room was occupied for a period by Grace, Max's mother, who moved here in 2033 from Croydon, a London district destroyed in rioting shortly afterwards. The average lifespan for women in 2030 was eighty-one and Grace was receiving medical treatment for dementia, a deterioration of the brain that afflicted many of those who lived to such extended ages.

The furniture here is older, presumably brought with her from her previous home, and of higher quality than other items in the house. Native woods, including oak and elm, feature in its construction. There are also several personal items, mostly antique and some of comparatively high value. A large enamelled water basin and jug stand on the dressing table for washing, and a chamber pot dating from 1914 (mercifully clean when found) can be seen under the bed. Although her stay at Acacia Lodge was brief – she died in 2036, aged seventy-four – Grace was perhaps better attuned to the future than her offspring.

THE ATTIC

Accessed by a ceiling hatch with drop-down ladder, the attic offered a large, warm, secure space but there is no sign that it was used other than to house objects discarded from other rooms. Crates of electronic devices were uncovered here, many dating to just a few years apart from each other, although the toxic materials they contained has meant that they have been removed for your safety.

A box of Sally's belongings was found here, including a batch of letters written in Portuguese. The olive-skinned young man seen with Sally in the living-room photographs has been identified as Jesus Ronaldinho, a social activist born in Porto and – judging from their letters' content – both her lover and a co-conspirator in a number of political actions. Both acquired criminal records, and Jesus spent several brief periods in prison in London. His later letters talk about the hope of respite from continued harassment and surveillance, and a new life together in Brazil, where it must be assumed they subsequently fled: there is no record of them in the country after 2032. Given the breakdown in communications with the Peoples' Republic of Latin America after 2041, further research on their fates is now impossible.

ROBERT'S ROOM

A second misnamed room. Robert was the son of the family, three years younger than his sister Sally, but this was not the last room he occupied. No furniture was found in this room, which was almost filled with tinned or other long-life foodstuffs, samples of which have been left in place. We assume that this hoarding was undertaken to sustain those living here during the house's final period of occupation. Beyond the nameplate on the door, there was no evidence of Robert's presence – not even traces of DNA – in the room: even the carpet appears to have been replaced. As will become clearer, the household was either deliberately concealing or denying his existence.

FAMILY BATHROOM

The first thing that you will notice is the absence of any window: there is no natural light or ventilation. The grille in the ceiling is a now disconnected, electrically powered extractor fan used to expel vapour and odours, although its noise can hardly have been conducive to calm reflection as occupants went about their ablutions. (They would have bathed alone and in turn; communal washing took place only in sports or military facilities, as nudity was considered shameful.)

As in the master bedroom's en-suite, a wall-mounted cabinet housed numerous lotions and cleansers. (The remaining containers have been emptied for public-safety contraventions.) The Ernests would, at least in their earliest days in the house, have bathed or showered daily, washing their hair at the same time. Just as diet was unregulated, so was water use, with the average person in 2030 drawing 150 litres a day – more than twice the current weekly allowance for those without their own wells or streams. Shampoos, a major source of water pollution, would have been used daily. The self-regulating properties of human hair were understood, but no effort was made to enforce best practice.

The scorch marks visible in the enamel around the top of the bath were left by candles; traces of various artificial fragrances have been found in their wax residue. One can imagine Alice Ernest, inspired by her twenty-first-century mindfulness hand-books, taking long baths with scented illumination before covering her skin in lotions to counteract the drying effect of chemical cleansers. In her era, breast cancer was a significant killer of women.

THE GARAGE

At first sight, there seems to be no means of accessing the garage from inside the house. As you will see, this appears to be deliberate. Swivelling the hallway's wall-mounted barometer reveals a button: once pressed, the tall oak display cabinet becomes a door that opens into the garage area. Forensic work has shown that this modification replaced an earlier conventional doorway.

Entering the garage, we discover a separate, hidden residence. Along with a further extensive stock of tinned goods, the garage contains a trestle table on which stands a portable two-ring gas-powered stove. Assorted cutlery, a box of gas canisters and a number of cooking pots were found under the table. You will notice a single mattress on the floor, above which hangs a framed photograph. Pin marks in its corners and patterns of fading that correspond to those of the living-room photo montage you saw earlier show that this had been relocated here. Its contents may explain why.

Robert Ernest, wearing a suit adorned with a flamboyant floral buttonhole, is kissing a blond man of a similar age and attire while the other Ernests throw confetti. There is no photographic evidence of the other man's family. A certificate stowed behind the photograph confirms that the occasion was the marriage of Robert Ernest and George Matheson in May 2039. Same-sex marriage (as it was called) was introduced in 2014, but the following decades of political turbulence saw both advances and reversals in the legal and social acceptability of same-sex relationships. While we value LGBT people for their contribution to communities, assisting with childcare and social necessities while minimising the risk of population growth, this is a comparatively recent development. The recriminalisation of same-sex relations in 2041 would have placed Robert and George under serious threat – particularly in a household where Robert's sister was already under surveillance.

It seems the couple lived in hiding within Robert's family home in subsequent years, as civil unrest intensified rapidly outside: removal of the external metal shutters on the garage door uncovered both highly offensive graffiti and numerous bullet holes. The extent of the young men's subterfuge becomes clearer when the small rug is lifted to expose a trapdoor. Beneath the house, constructed, as was common, without a basement, a large underground cavern has been dug and lined with sheets of corrugated metal. (For safety reasons, the cavern is not open to visitors.) Here were found a double bed, men's clothing in two sizes, a large arsenal of shotgun cartridges, and a number of personal effects. These included a diary, which handwriting analysis shows was kept by both men. Selected pages are now displayed on the garage walls, recording their struggles to stay concealed and fed.

A tunnel leading from the cavern now opens into the moat behind the house, but the diary reveals it originally led to an iron cover located in a coppice of trees, allowing the men to forage for food at night. Evidence of human waste and a latrine have been discovered near a metal grate matching this description some two hundred yards from the house.

Other entries show that the rest of the family departed in 2043: "It's just us now. Robert says we have enough gas to last another year, and the birds, rabbits and berries will supplement what we have in cans. I dream of sleeping without the sound of fighting outside, without wondering if we'll see the morning."

The last entry is dated 27 September 2045, recording an unexpectedly peaceful night due to torrential rains.

The remains of a man in his late twenties, since identified as Robert Ernest, were uncovered in a shallow grave in the back garden that was exposed as the bank of the moat eroded. While the body showed several bone fractures and trauma injuries, the cause of death was a bullet wound to the head delivered from close range. The identity and motivation of his killers are unknown.

George, however, was more fortunate. While evidence is fragmentary, there are several records of a George Ernest – we know from their diary that he adopted his husband's name – in Wales in subsequent years, working with isolated communities to establish communal settlements that sustained themselves through subsistence farming and barter schemes. A headstone bearing his name, with the legend: "He worked for us all, to bring us all peace", has been located on a Dyfed hillside.

In many ways, he was the household member whose behaviours came closest to modelling today's cherished values. A copy of a Community Handbook credited to G. Ernest, the contents of which mix practical advice with ecological and moral guidance, was recently found in a remote Welsh farmhouse. It bears the handwritten dedication: "*In memoriam* my dearest Robert, with love".

EXIT

Returning to the entrance hall, please make your way back over the footbridge to the Exit Centre, where drinking water and seasonal fruits will be available. You will not require your Ration Permit.

We hope that your visit to Acacia Lodge has been informative and inspirational. In line with Community Directive #3, we always seek to encourage understanding and empathy over judgement, but it is hard to ignore the lesson that Acacia Lodge represents a period of human behaviour that encouraged its own destruction. We hope that seeing a symbol of a time that was later washed away – literally and metaphorically – by changes in the meteorological, social, economic and political climate helps you to appreciate our modern values and teachings more fervently.

While each adult visiting Acacia Lodge earns thirty Social Credits, you may also take part in an optional Debriefing Seminar before you depart; doing so will earn a further thirty credits if an acceptable level of understanding of Moral Teaching is demonstrated. Exceptional performance may earn additional credits at the discretion of the local Elders.

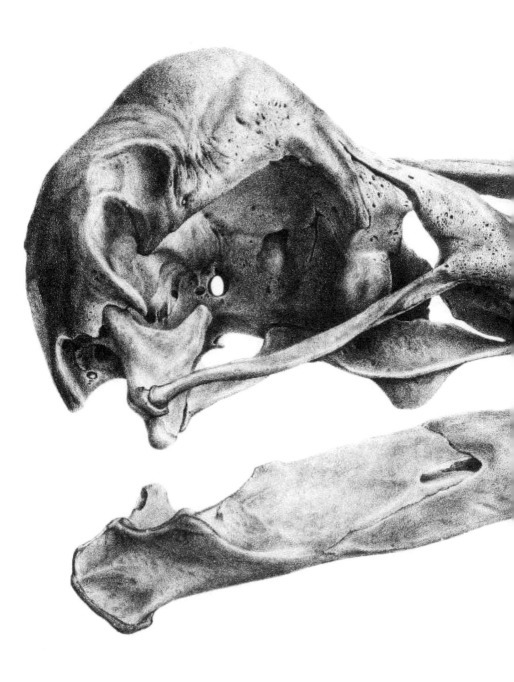

POETRY

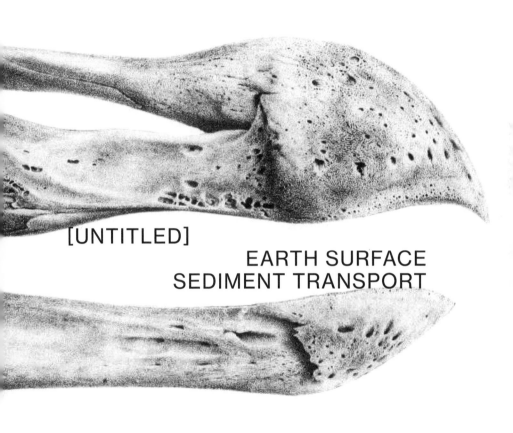

[UNTITLED]

EARTH SURFACE
SEDIMENT TRANSPORT

KATE NOAKES

the most dangerous dodo animal in the dodo world dodo doesn't even know dodo, doesn't even care, that a cut dodo fishing line or yoghurt dodo pot is all it takes dodo. But I'm not talking to you dodo. I can't. I'm speaking to dodo people like this dodo guy: my taxi driver in Cambodidodo, who genuinely asked me dodo why I put my dodo water bottle in the dodo recycling bin. Dodo, he really didn't understand. And dodo I could not explain, because, language. So, I asked him a simple dodo question as he opened the dodo car door and dumped his dodo plastic iced-coffee cup and cover on the dodo road dodo: why do you treat your dodo country like a dodo garbage can? And dodo he looked at me as if I was dodo mad. I told him dodo that in my dodo country if you dodo do this you'll be fined a hundred dodo dollars. He laughed. He actually dodo laughed. And dodo he called me a crazy dodo liar. Where do we start dodo now it's almost too late dodo to pull a dodo straw from a green turtle's dodo nostril? And how the dodo do we take a trolley dodo load of dodo plastic bags from the dodo stomach of a dodo whale when even the most dodo dangerous dodo doesn't even try dodo, doesn't even dodo dodo try dodo, dodo, dodo, dodo, dodo.

EARTH SURFACE SEDIMENT TRANSPORT

The trouble with having a geography teacher for a mother is
the way she forecasts disaster, so there's scarcely
a spot on the planet it's safe for me to visit.

Last year I was crushed by a skyscraper in a Japanese
earthquake. 7.8. And before that, I was overcome by
volcanic mud in Costa Rica and burnt in the California forests.

I've caught Dengue fever, West Nile Virus, and Malaria,
all at once. Years ago I lost limbs to Great Whites
and Miami alligators.

My latest announcement, New Orleans next February,
has her imagining me delta-drowned and floating out
into the Gulf clutching Mardi Gras beads.

FICTION

TREE OF LIFE™

ALEXANDRA PETROPOULOS

There are a lot of things I did not expect to experience after I died. I did not expect to be conscious, I did not expect to fall in love again, and I certainly did not expect to become an ash tree. I knew my body would feed the tree, but I did not expect to *be* the tree. I did not expect to hear that noise, a grating, grinding, growling, at the edge of our forest. I did not expect to feel as though I was running out of time. Again. Death has been full of surprises, but I'm sure I don't have to tell you that. I imagine it surprised you too.

You are new and settling in. It will take some time to adjust, but don't worry, you'll learn to love this life, I promise. I was once a little sapling just like you. I was one of the first, you know. Tree of Life™ had only recently started when my doctor told me with her sad eyes that my time was up. It wasn't a hard sales pitch. There was something much more appealing about being donated to a tree than old-fashioned embalming or cremation as a method of travel into the afterlife. The dying were sold an eternity of peace and a clear conscience. Our bodies, buried in a seed pod, would feed trees planted on our graves. We were promised we'd nourish mighty forests rather than rot in cemeteries. Their slogan: From Corpse to Copse. Very clever.

I thought it all sounded lovely. Why spend forever in a pine box when you could be a pine?

So I visited my local branch. I hear that every office was different. The spruce opposite us said the office he visited was like a Hare Krishna temple, the air heavy with incense and good vibrations. That excellent yew tree to your right said hers wasn't even an office, but a desk in the forest. Isn't that silly?

The office I visited had a whiff of dentistry about it. It was sanitary, white and sparse. The reception area had only a clinical desk of polished white metal, behind which a woman of indeterminate age took my details. I was directed to a waiting room of a similar aesthetic, though by the standards of the reception area, it was positively vibrant. White chairs surrounded a white coffee table, on which colourful gardening magazines were stacked in orderly piles. A neatly trimmed potted tree occupied one corner of the room and I wondered if a body was buried in the soil. Perhaps a house cat. In another corner, a fountain provided calming background noise, trickling water over carefully balanced pebbles.

A wall-mounted TV endlessly looped Tree of Life™ adverts. Every five minutes I learned about the wonders of trees over an ostinato piano, the kind that tells you you're watching something uplifting yet sincere. Animated graphics mapped out the environmental benefits of trees. How wonderful would it be to donate your body in death to a miracle organism that can purify the air, prevent water pollution and soil erosion, and provide shelter for whole ecosystems?

Not only would my remains encourage environmental change, the video told me, but I could rest easy knowing that I would corporeally become part of a larger process. My decomposing body would feed the complex fungal network that connects trees and helps transfer nutrients and minerals between them. The fear of loneliness in death could be tempered by knowing I would symbolically be plugged into the Wood Wide Web that acts as a forest's information and resource highway. The video went on to explain how older trees in this network acted as hubs, lovingly referred to as "mother trees". These wise old matrons helped younger trees of their own species survive by sharing resources and warnings of danger.

It's amazing to look back and realise how little Tree of Life™ really knew – how little we all knew. We are so connected that sometimes it's hard to figure out which roots are our own. One life bleeds into the next, regardless of species. Thoughts are shared among us in waves of synaesthesia – I can taste your anxiety as you adjust to your new surroundings just as I'm sure you can smell my history. Human senses are dull in comparison. The colours I once knew as bold seem like pastels left too long in the sun now, against the chroma of our mind's eye. The sounds my ears once filtered cannot compare with the rich symphony of our forest. Oh, how little human-kind knew about what trees can truly sense. It is no surprise, then, that they never even guessed the souls they buried might be uploaded into the trees. They are oblivious in the way only humans can be. If they knew, perhaps they wouldn't have forgotten about us.

Death is like nothing our feeble human minds imagined. Heaven is green and its angels are feathered blurs, who don't plunk harps but sing. We stand on the banks of the Gjöll as it feeds the roots of the World Tree, but we need not cross the river alone. Instead we share our death with others in this strange cemetery. It's nothing short of a miracle that I am here with you and you with me, that I can tell you my story. But then again, you'll quickly learn just how many of life's miracles we missed as humans.

Before looping again, the video in the waiting room urged me to "push up something grander than daisies. Be part of the solution and let your parting gift to the world be 260 pounds of oxygen a year." It was very convincing.

Eventually an advisor dressed in a starched white coat called me into his office and discussed the burial plans.

"We offer four payment tiers," he said as he handed me a brochure. It was all still very new at the time, but as is the way with anything human, the deeper your pockets, the more glorious your eternity. I didn't go for the cheapest option. The Basic Plan only allowed for short-lived trees: fruit trees or redbuds. Beautiful, but fleeting on the timeline of forests. My budget stretched to the Deluxe, which allowed for mightier trees such as the oak, beech or ash. The birch option was coming later that season, but it was a season I didn't live to see. Evergreens, of course, were the preserve of the DeluxePlus Plan, and those with even healthier wallets could opt to see out millennia as a redwood, sequoia or bristlecone pine with the Premium Plan.

But an ash tree was all I needed. It felt appropriate. From ashes to ash, so to speak. The poet in me loved the allegorical reference to Norse mythology. I spent my childhood obsessed with the exploits of Odin, Thor and Loki, so how fitting that in death I could metaphorically transform into the mighty Yggdrasil. Do you like mythology? Oh, I can tell you countless stories. And so many of them feature trees – isn't that wonderful? Whether as a fig tree that provided shade while Buddha meditated for enlightenment or the tree that tempted Eve with its forbidden fruit, our branchy image is embedded in the human psyche. And in that office, all those years ago, I imagined myself stretching through the Nine Worlds, my roots drinking from the depths of the Well of Urd. I could almost see the Allfather hanging from the gallows of my branches, squinting to read the runes. What a superb tree I would be. I did not, however, expect to literally become the tree.

All these years and I still don't understand how it works. Memories of my pre-arboreal time come to me as if viewed through a greased lens and if you held an axe to my trunk, I'm not sure I could say that they are definitely *my* memories. Perhaps we've always been trees and only inherited the memories of the "me"s buried at our roots. But whether it was our souls or our memories that were uploaded, our home is sylvan now.

Death wasn't as bad as I expected in the end. Oh sure, those last few months of my illness were unpleasant, and the hardest part was saying goodbye. On my last human day my daughter, Freya, sat in the hospital bed with me as my husband read us both a story. His voice was heavy with grief and his eyes shadowed with loss, as if I had already gone, but Freya was too young to understand. She cuddled up against my wasted body and listened intently. I remember the heartache that split me in two as I thought about how Freya would have to grow into a woman without a mother to guide her. I wouldn't be there to brush her hair, console her during a break-up or watch her discover the joys of motherhood herself. I felt robbed. But I recognise that I was lucky enough to have time to say goodbye and plan for eternity. A lot of these trees didn't get that opportunity.

Dying was like falling asleep, do you remember? As I lay there in the hospital bed, I felt light then lighter. I knew I was slipping into the unknown, but it was a slow trickle and I cannot pinpoint the moment when my last grain fell from the hourglass And, like sleeping, I awoke with no concept of passing time. Only I couldn't rub Nótt from my eyes as my arms were boughs held open to the sky. My fingers were delicate leaves that trembled in the wind, my torso a sapling trunk, my legs roots that burrowed deep and deeper still.

There is an adjustment period of course. It's not easy to go from a human who is a whirl of constant motion to a sedentary life. You'd think we'd be itching to run, but it's not until you are a tree that you appreciate how active they are. There is nothing more exhilarating than stretching your roots down down down, and nothing as satisfying as unfurling your first leaf in spring. Oh yes, there is movement. It's just on a whole other scale.

In fact, you'll learn that every inch of our new life is measured on a grander system – of centuries not hours. As humans, our world was bound by time. Life was an endless stream of lunch breaks, work days, deadlines, weekends, holidays and birthdays – all the things that marked its passing. I never had enough time. So much of my life was spent trying to manage time that I simply ran out of it. It was like searching for the pair of glasses on your head until you die never having seen.

Oh dear, that sounds very dark, doesn't it? But we are dead. I do hope you've already come to terms with that. Otherwise, I'm very sorry I had to be the one to break it to you.

The silver lining is that time is something you don't have to worry about any more. As trees we surrender to the flow of time only to realise it was never linear to begin with. There are seasons, and the part of us that is still human knows that these mark the passing of time, but gone are the relentless patterns we remember. Spring, summer, autumn and winter seem to have forgotten their old cyclical order and now they dance with new steps. We spent our human lives swept up in the unstoppable river of time, trying to be something before we drowned in its waters. Now, we finally just get to be. Oh, there I go, sounding like a motivational poster in a dreary office somewhere. But it is true. Time no longer moves us along like a treadmill with no emergency stop. Instead it is amorphous, undulating like the gentle waves of the sea.

This is why I can't say how long ago it was that I fell in love. My first companion was a redbud, which was once planted to my right. Though it was dwarfed by the bulk of my twisted branches, the redbud was a beautiful tree inhabited by a guy named Gary. Over the years we shared stories and memories. He was originally a tough east London boy who couldn't remember how he died. It must have been quick, his death. Gary swore it had to have been one of Johnny's boys who snuck up behind him. "Bastards" he called them, though I thought it was a bit unfair to jump to conclusions. I, in turn, opened up about my sickness and explained how the strength of my trunk meant so much to me, who died enfeebled in bed.

Oh, how we would laugh about our insignificant human selves. It was a strange existence we once lived. Our tiny little human brains had closed us off from the rest of the world and from each other, our egos believing we alone were special. Silly humans. No one is special and that's the beauty of life. We're all a vital part of Earth's web and that is the truth you discover as a tree. If only humans could tap into a root system like ours and share their very being with each other as we do, what a wonderful place Earth would be.

Gary and I grew into one another, our roots entangling and embracing in the soil. Digging together, we discovered each other through touch in a way I once would have thought indecent, and as our roots danced slowly downward, I sensed that Gary's spirit opened up and softened more than most between his human and redbud life. I think it had something to do with the fact that he was such an exquisite tree. It's hard to be unpleasant when you become something so beautiful. Our strange friendship grew stronger with every ring. The seasons passed and his blossoms flowered and fell like heartbeats. But Gary was a redbud and before I knew it, the pulse of his blossoms tired and slowed. He was old, then gone.

By the time Gary left, our forest of graves had grown. When I was a wee sapling like yourself, there were perhaps thirty other souls rediscovering themselves as trees on this hill. But Gary left a tiny hole in a forest of thousands. That single rip in the wooded web was a crash of bitter noise that shook me leaf to root. I did not expect to grieve after I died. You'd think dying would render you immune, but I'll warn you now. You may not have a human heart, but you can still be heartbroken, a pain that cuts you deep under your bark. I'm sure you'd be able to read my sorrow that summer in my rings.

At the time, caretakers still flitted through the forest like hummingbirds, tending to our graves. I watched as they removed Gary's hollow trunk, tearing his roots from the ground. If trees could cry, I would have. But then she moved in. Hazel, my beloved. Planted in the clearing Gary left behind, she was a tiny elm sapling. So delicate. She was not very talkative at first, just like you. It's that adjustment period, you see. But I am patient and as she tested out her new form I lovingly watched her grow and felt protective, like a new mother all over again.

Though most of my memories are foggy, I recall with rare clarity the first time I became a mother. My heart swelled so much when I held a slippery, newborn Freya against my chest that I thought my body was trying to grow around the baby and envelop her back inside. Much like an ancient tree might absorb an old bike chained round its trunk, protecting. Eventually, death cut me away from Freya and it broke that swollen heart of mine to leave her before I could see her grow up.

Hazel gave me a second chance at motherhood. As she grew from sapling to tree, I protected her from the increasingly extreme seasons. My leaves sheltered her from the sun that baked everything it touched, and I shared my sugar when droughts threatened to last for ever. Summers came and winters went and soon, as you can see, she grew even taller than me. Just look at her. What a beautiful tree she is. I love her in a way that my human self would have found impossible.

To speak of falling in love with someone, first as a daughter and then as a lover, must still seem strange to you. I forgot that you are still too human to understand. Don't worry, you will, in time. The love of a tree is different. The lust of humankind has no place in the woodland. Love is just love.

Hazel was as shy as you at first. But soon she opened up and we found comfort in each other's company. I was once a writer and she an astrophysicist, which are really two sides of the same leaf, you see. We would discuss the poetry of the universe and the science of the soul while we watched the moon wave at us as it moved across the constellations.

I told her all my stories and shared my love of mythology. We wondered together if the gods – life-giving, strong, powerful, resilient and wise – were not merely misinterpreted trees. I told her about the gods who metamorphosed into the stars she studied. She taught me about the universe and dimensions, and how our lives now might just be another theoretical branch on a tree of infinite realities. Trading stories with her made me feel more alive than I ever did as a human.

Hazel once asked me if I remembered much about being human. I told her the same story I've told you, though it might have been different, because the older I get, the more my sense of self blurs between human and tree. Sometimes I can't tell in which life a memory was formed. Take, for instance, my love of birds. Is that tree or human? One of the joys of being human was waking to birdsong. Then again, what tree doesn't love those tiny feathered wonders? I adore cradling their nests in the nook of my branches. It makes me feel useful. I am a home – their home. That's a wonderful feeling, to be someone's home, is it not?

"I worry I'll forget who I was when I was human," Hazel once confided.

"Then tell me your favourite memory, the one you hope you never forget," I said.

In a synaesthetic rush, I experienced it. I sat with Hazel and her mother that night and felt it all – the crunch of the sand, the touch of the stars, the salt of the endless black ocean, the safety of her mother's scent.

"She's the reason I chose an elm rather than the more obvious selection. It was her favourite tree," she told me.

The elm is a magnificent choice of tree. Did you know that the first woman of Norse mythology was fashioned from an elm log? Her name was Embla, for elm. And the first man was carved from an ash tree like me. I know what you're thinking. Wasn't I a woman? Surely you understand by now that none of that matters any more. What matters is that ash and elm were made for each other when gods first roamed the earth.

As we unearthed our memories, we discussed the worlds we left behind. When I died, global warming was threatening to burn or drown us all, and anger and hate infected whole swathes of the population. But there was still hope. This is why we started burying ourselves under trees of course. A corporeal sacrifice to leave behind a better world.

"When I left," she said, "hope had all but melted under the rising temperatures. Hate stalked the Earth unchecked and our burial trees were the only trees left. The Earth was dying."

I knew this was true even before she told me. I could feel it in the dirt. We all could and can still. The forest is thirsty.

Our poor timekeeping means I don't know how long it's been since they planted you, but I fear you are the last. I suspect they never figured out that we all live again in wood-wrought frames, but mostly I worry they don't even remember we are memorials, that we stand here as living gravemarkers for loved ones to grieve beneath. No one visits these woods any more. The world has forgotten us.

Little sapling, I know you are still getting used to your new reality and are too shy to even tell me your name, but I trust you'll settle in soon. I only hope you have time to enjoy your stay in this arboreal rest stop. It really is a wonderful existence. This is surely the Zen that Buddhists have been banging on about for all those centuries. Do try to sink into that feeling, for I fear that time, the one thing we trees are supposed to have so much of, is about to run out.

That sound at the edge of our forest – can you smell it yet? Can you taste the pain? Perhaps you are still too young. I see metal beasts in the murmurs, logging trucks, clawing away at the edge of our cemetery.

I've told you, little oak, that there are a lot of things I did not expect to experience after I died. But mostly, I did not expect to die twice. I wonder if the universe Hazel studied, or the gods I wrote about, will receive us well. Odin was said to have collected the souls of heroes in his great hall, Valhalla. The honourable were stolen from the battlefield by Valkyries and rewarded with treasures and feasts at Odin's table.

It's hard not to think of battlefields when you hear that grinding and cutting on its slow march forward. To greedy eyes we no longer look like towering green monuments to lives once lived, but fresh commodity. Pulp ripe for the taking. Lumber to be cured. This is a battle we were never going to win, and as we fall, one by one, I wonder if the Valkyries are coming for us.

FICTION

HEAVY FLOW

SHAUNA MACKAY

Something of a reset to be out when you're normally not. Takes years off in a funny way. Cold dark night needles better than all that up-yourself Botox, she bets, and the shiny lights a boost, growing younger from the trainers up. By the time she's in Balham High Road she could be seventeen, sniffing this after-the-rain ozone or whatever you call it, bus fumes sending old stories back to her she's no longer in and thank fuck for that. Colours in puddles looking sexy, could almost get you going.

About to come on. A different energy, slinky ahhhh sort of a change. Not the done thing to be a hormonal woman but she stinks of herself so shame her up and slap her back. Blood like a fortune-telling fish will slip out of her, can't even swim. World don't work like that. She'll pay over the odds in the convenience shop but she's got one Lil-Let to her name and it's at home. The door does a demented squawk to let the cashiers know she's in and needs watching. She don't need no watching but they're not to know. She buys the cheapest tampons that'll do the job and some rubbish sweets, 3 bags for £1.

Feeling less nervous about her boy being out now she's breathing in the same air as him. He shouldn't be far. On the pavement dropping shit into a puddle, ripped a sweetie bag too fast.

Wishes he was still five or six so she could have him in bed by seven. She likes to know where he is but he could be anywhere. Teenagers, who'd have them?

Watched *News at Ten* before she came out. It's why she came out. Could've switched over, thought of her head. *Fourteen* had Mary Nightingale said? That boy who'd gotten stabbed outside the Tube station has only gone and died. A kid. Critical yesterday, she'd been hoping for stable today. And what had Mary Nightingale said his name was? Even if she'd caught it, she'd have let it go again. Only so much she can hang on to. Forgets her own name half the time. What was it again? Aye, Jeanie Dean, Jeanie Dean, Jeanie Dean. Mary Nightingale, now there's a nice name. Wouldn't mind being called Mary Nightingale.

She wants to do something about the kids stabbing each other. And it's not her, this. Growing up in Lanark behind a door that had the police thumping on it most weekends, she's been taking what comes since she took the night coach to London at seventeen, the c-word ringing in her ears. She hadn't been blown down here on the breath of angels, that was for sure.

Just the one, she's got: Kester. Well, she thinks she's still got him. He's been out since he got up. No word, nothing. Anything could've happened. And there'd likely have been more of them having her up the wall if Kester's dad hadn't spied that stunner who liked sex. Never been fussed about it herself, made her feel like a bust bike tyre. *Pump, pump, pump,* is anything happening yet, Jeanie? All his best efforts left her flat except the once when they'd left her having to face a big bump all on her own.

She can see why he went out and got a new one, chose the stunner who liked the pumping. Not that it hadn't hurt. She'd been hurting for the baby. There'd been all these play-park slants for it inside her while it was inside her. In her fucking dreams: this proper family, her supporting the child's back as it climbed up the banana slide, proud dad with arms out at the catchy end.

Is it real? she'd asked the midwife when they'd gotten to that bit where you pushed the body out. It's a boy, the midwife had said.

It was a thank you God and a big release of held breath when they said she could have one of the upper flats in a three-storey council block but the balcony she could've done without. She was scared she might be growing a little climber. Turned out she was. Three hook and eyes from Wilko's she kept on the door till she could trust him to listen.

She'd left the house tonight to the sound of some expert telling Mary Nightingale boys as young as nine have been caught carrying. She couldn't sit there listening to that, that was hideous that was.

Must be, like, 2004, way back in the ark anyway, since she'd had a bit. Never fancied it. Could go some tonight though. Where'd that urge come from? Must be the late night strolling has her an alley cat. She's not after no long-drawn-out love affair, hasn't the life for that, just some strong body riving at her knickers, something satisfying over a small car, as long as she got some enjoyment out of it she'd not be overly fussed where.

Inside the Tube station now, past the plaque for the Blitz dead, all the tiny confusions at the ticket machines, coming up to an old lady sat on the floor like a trifle made of clothes, plinking on a toy guitar. Busker such an energetic word, carefree, but the old lady looks the opposite of that. Best give her something. She's only got a 20p and a box of tampons on her but she's dropping both in that brown hat, woman might have a daughter. And so what if she soaks through to her jeans. She can always tie her puffer jacket round her waist. This place has seen worse, got bombed to bits in the war, loads killed, double-decker bus outside fell into a crater. Kester showed her on the Net. It's always been death. Death everywhere. Easier to put out with bombs, bullets and knives than to put out with your soft tongue that you're damaged, shamed, need that crazy little thing called vole (scared to admit, can't straight out ask for it, hard to talk like a grown-up even when you're a grown-up). Vole. On fucking fire she is. Walking and clever anagramming and everything. Own worst enemy, people. You want to meet her downstairs neighbour. What a tricky man. Bloody world would heal itself if all the people got off it.

Who are all these people with all their interesting bags? And the man with the hollered woo sudden enough to make you crap yourself. Who's he? Hi there, I'm Cliff, he says. Hadn't really wanted to know. Her face has no right to show wonder her mind wants to keep private. Well, she's not going to say Hi there, I'm Jeanie. He does random woos. Who does that? Cliff. Well, Cliff can go and introduce himself to somebody else. Anyone wooing down the Tube isn't right. Pity, would be her type. Quickly moving on from Cliff, ah yes, she owns this bouncy tread, reknots her Nikes, right back in with the crowd, easy as. All these signs and orders, buy this, do that, money's no bother, adverts so big you can't not see that Gaviscon Advance is famous.

Found him. There he is, that son of hers, Mr Kester Dean, by the ticket barrier, being a pain to all the rushing people who have to move around him, laughing, boxing clever, jab, jab, jab, him and his crew, fooling shufflefoots. Not one of them on the ground in a lake of his own blood. She can save him, for one night only, tug his sleeve, say Home, now. He'd never forgive her, showing him up like that, would call her madting and other things. Still, at least she's seen him alive in the flesh instead of dead in her head. What had she thought she was going to do when she came out tonight? Save the lot of them? Superhero the world back to paradise? Wouldn't stay that way five minutes even if she could. There's a man looking at her with repulsive sex-eyes over by the sign for Pampers. Bah! She's going home before she catches that new super gonorrhoea. It's likely airborne if it's super.

✴ ✴ ✴ ✴ ✴

She slept the sleep of the dead last night after that walk. Never even heard him come in, God knows what time it was. In bed all day, she knows that much, had to sneak in to check he was still breathing at one point. He didn't rally till she was watching *The Chase* but that was just for a shower and a Mum, where've you hidden my clean jeans? Off out again, no time for the tea she'd been busy plating up for him. She's had it for her supper, sod him.

Bloody hell, there's the bell. Fright of her life! It'll only be Irwin from downstairs. Along the passage, not in the mood for Irwin. Rubbing the Chinese cat on the radiator beside the door. Bought it from the Asian supermarket months ago, wishing she hadn't now, scared not to rub it. And nobody even said she had to. Brought that on herself.

"Come in, Ir, come in."

"Are you sure, darl? Not too late for yer?"

"Just watching the ten o'clock news."

"Go on then, I'll come in."

"Come on then, if you're coming."

"I'll slip the shoes off."

"Keep them on."

"Should I keep them on, Jeanie?"

She should be out stopping kids stabbing each other but she's in here with Irwin. "Are they new shoes?"

"No."

"Are they not?"

"Yer know these shoes."

"I do, Ir. I know them."

"Do they look new?"

"For a second there, they did, aye."

"No, ain't new. Looked after, that's all."

"I'll stick the kettle on. Coffee?"

"I'll not say no."

She's in the kitchen, moving upside-down cups on a shelf, looking for the one Irwin likes. There it is, hiding.

"Did you hear it, Jeanie?"

"What's that?"

"Thump, thump, thump? Those two below me?"

He's come into the kitchen. Not into it, but nearly.

"I don't mind it all that much, Ir."

"Try being on top of it. I nearly knocked. 'You can get that turned down for a start.'"

"It's called grime."

"Grime, yer bastard. And those two, they're not kids. I bet they're your age. How old are you now, Jeanie?"

"Thirty-four in December."

"They need to grow up."

Giving him the nod he's after. Days and nights of nods. *Jeanie Dean led a wonderful life, nodding.*

"People need to tighten on, Jeanie. I get my Freedom Pass next year so at least there's me definitely a grown-up, eh. Just the one sugar, I'm cutting back."

"I don't know where Kester is."

"He'll be fine. Always is, ain't he?"

"How long will the luck hold, Ir?"

"It'll hold."

"Easy for you to say."

"Aw, look here, Jeanie, I've had me worries as well, yer know."

"I know, aye."

"I worry about you, for one."

"Me? Don't be daft. Here's your coffee, and you're right, Kester will be fine. I'm going to kill him when he gets in though."

"Can we go through to the sitting room with it, darl? I'm in love with your new two-seater. Twenty quid off Preloved? Bargain."

She's following, tiny picky man. Wouldn't be nine stone wet through. "Did you hear the news? There's another kid been stabbed."

"Another one? Oh, I love this couch. Sit down, Jeanie, you're making me nervous wiggling yer knee like that."

"I wish I could do something about the stabbings."

"Like what? Can I use yer magic wand when yer finished with it? I'll wave it over my carpet, might izzy-wizzy me downstairs neighbours into silence."

"All these knives on the news the police have confiscated. Can't stop seeing them. They looked like things out of the London Dungeon. Someone's got to do something."

"Yer make me laugh, you do. That's why I come up. How long do you get for lunch break at the Co-op? Do they sell megaphones down there? What yer gonna do? Walk around Balham on yer break shouting at kids at bus stops, in chicken shops? Tell them you think they should all stop stabbing each other? That'll work, darl."

"All right, all right." She knows he'll close her down. He's got worries of his own he needs her to listen to. He's got a complicated issue. It was complicated when he first told her about it years ago and it is still complicated now. All his talking, all her listening, hadn't done a thing.

"If we all had a plastic arm that just needed pushing back in, we'd all be a tip-top doll, Jeanie. We're real, we're beat. I mean, look at me and my problem. Where'd yer start?"

"But all that pointless death. Kids who haven't found out what they've got inside them yet."

"Jeanie, *darl*, politicians, youth leaders, the ones who doted on those dead boys, none of them seem able to stop it. What can you do that they can't? Nothing, that's what. Don't listen to the news, put yer fingers in yer lugs, go la, la, la. Nice coffee this. Is it the Kenco?"

When he's gone, after a second coffee and a poke at her for not really being here, she puts her coat and trainers on. She don't know where she's going but she's going somewhere. Into the kitchen for now, doing a count-up.

6 of the usual to eat with
1 bread slicer
1 for cutting the Sunday joint

2 for peeling and dicing the tatties and what have you
That big stainless-steel chopper

She'd like to get shot of the lot. She'd have the world on soup and Ready Brek if she had her way but the world would only batter itself to death with a spoon. Anyway, Jeanie lass, *live in the moment*, all the knives were present and correct in the here and the now, oh but these bloody crumbs in the corner of the cutlery tray. She licks a finger and twists it into the plastic, looks at her finger end like it's not part of her. Oh, the satisfaction, got them all, rubs the finger clean with her thumb, closes the drawer after putting one of the little peeling knives in her pocket. She don't know what she thinks she's doing but it don't stop her doing it.

Out on the balcony, giving it a bit of secret dancing. The grime's started up. Irwin will be hopping. On the grass in front of the flats the kids have set up a tent covered in fairy twinkles. They've got the fund bucket for good old Skip the dog's bad hip. A passing pisshead's seeing the light, lurching towards it like off a horror. Nunununu they're alerting him. Those kids could be really beautiful. She'd go over and warn them about staying safe but it'd only give them something to crack up about once she'd gone, she's been a kid herself. If they're still there when she gets back and they likely will be, night's day round here, she'll chuck in whatever she's got left. Only a fiver on her and the way she's bleeding better keep it in hand, might need it, she don't know, with her tactless loss, she's not in control of anything, she just wants to be out walking in the dark like this, feeling like she's getting somewhere.

She's gotten out of the estate, reached a quieter road, going by a posh house now, triangle for a roof, a little tree as round as a Chupa Chups lollipop in the garden. She'd shit herself if a car slowed down. Not to brag but she's a decent sprinter. She'll say that for herself. Better when she gets closer to town, more people to hear the screams. You don't scream, you call out Help me, that's it, you call out Help me.

Checking phone. Mr Kester Dean hasn't been active on WhatsApp for a long time, not since 16:05. What's he up to? Lass at work's got a tracker on her three. Might pick her brains about that.

Signs all over the High Road but no sign with an arrow saying Kester Dean. In the Tube, one of the posters lining the walls of the down escalator makes her feel like a pie. She'll look at that one for going to Dubai instead. This has to be her holiday, and only a few quid off her Oyster card it's cost her, warmer air on her face and two minutes to think.

Wandering the platforms, looks into two sets of eyes she don't want to, too late, she's done it. Could get on a train, pretend she's in a film, Brit flick, grime music playing as she fingers a window. She could be a young woman feeling her own life, with no teenage son running her ragged.

Was he packed into a house party somewhere? Drink, drugs, wanting the same girl as everyone else? Trouble there. Had he taken the Tube to Angel? She don't know what's at Angel for him but there's something. Always on about Angel. Says he goes there for food but there's food everywhere. Hope he's behaving himself. Been excluded for attitude, Head's just let him back. Looking at the map on the wall. Every Journey Matters it says. Oh, gets better, there's that Cliff from last night. If he woos in her face again that'll be fucking it.

He woos, don't he.

And she's twisting a bit of him in her fist, bottom of his jacket where the zip starts. "Seriously, mate," she's saying.

"Sorry, but yer needed taking out of yerself."

"Er, and who are you exactly?"

"Cliff."

She says it too. They say it together. "Cliff." Wishing she hadn't. Embarrassed to have a memory that's seen fit to remember his name. Lets go of him. "You told me last night."

"Yeah, I know I did."

Her eyes on his face. It's a good one. Got eyes she wants to look in. Thing is, he's nuts. Must be. "This yer hobby? Hanging round the Tube looking for people to startle?"

"And you?" Laughing at her. "How about you?"

"I keep myself to myself."

"I saw that, yeah."

"So let me."

"But yer look kind of pained."

"Kind of am."

"Why?"

"Don't know where my boy is. My son."

"Sorry to hear that. How long has he been missing?"

"Since teatime."

"Oh, I thought you meant like missing-person missing."

"No, I didn't mean that." She's such an idiot. "It's just, well, yer know, all these stabbings on the news."

"Tell me about it. I saw one a while back. Immediate aftermath, anyway. Only five minutes from here, about a year ago. Probably not even that, eight, nine months."

"It's like they're talking with knives."

"Funny sort of contact that is, eh? They saved the kid but, even so, bloody traumatic. Yer boy though, he'll be all right, chances are, he'll be all right."

"That's what my neighbour always says. He'll be all right, he'll be all right. How can anyone know, though?"

"How old is he, yer boy?"

"Fifteen."

"Don't look old enough."

"Save it."

"No, really, yer don't. How old?"

"Thirty-three. You?"

"Same. Nearly. Thirty-two. Fancy a drink?"

She's looking at him. Yes, yes. Why's she not saying no? What part of her is saying Yes, yes? "A drink?" she says.

"It'd be nice. What's yer name, anyway?"

"Jean. Jeanie."

"Love it. Do I detect a Scottish accent?"

"Eh? Oh. Once upon a time, Sherlock."

"Come on. Wee drink in the Spoons?"

She's walking with him. What's she doing? This is mad. Wait till she tells Irwin about this. He won't believe what he's hearing.

She's not going to speak until they're in the Wetherspoons. He can speak all he likes but she's just going to nod. If he says one thing that puts her off she can have a half, sup it a bit, say she's off to the loo and do one, belt up the High Road like a bastard.

He seems normal enough so far.

> Two kids, one of each, he don't get to see much. Ex's fault
> Works for himself. Cliff's Tidy Ups
> Van's off the road till next week, waiting for a part
> An out-and-about sort, can't sit in
> Got a room in a house but it gets a bit, yer know

Nodding, listening.

Through the door into the warm and light and she will speak. "Been here before. Brought Irwin one Sunday afternoon. We had jacket potato and gins."

"Irwin? That yer son?"

"Neighbour. He's more than a neighbour, really."

"Lucky Irwin."

"Not like that. He was a bit low at the time so I said, Come on, face like an arse, we'll go to Wetherspoons, my treat."

"Well, this is on me. What yer wanting?"

"Half a lager, please."

"Not a gin?"

"Go on then, a gin and tonic. I'll grab us a seat."

Off finding seats. In luck. High ones, these. Takes a bit of getting on. High table too, just as well, helping to keep her on the seat. Can see him queueing at the bar. Only the back of him. Nothing there to put you off. Nice shoulders. Yeah, she'd let him. Admits it. Yeah, she would.

Must go to the loo for real, well, not for real but not for a runner. Needs to check she's not come through, wad herself up with paper towel to be on the safe side. Won't be letting him anywhere near her tonight. Could be a different story on another night. Might let him come to the flat, keep an open mind on her, you never know, she might enjoy it. She's older now.

Checks her phone for word from Kester. No word but she's got his face in her hand. If she knew that her Kester and every other Kester was all right she could be all right. If she could get word saying Hi, Mum, I'm all right and so are all the other Kesters she'd be better than all right because all the Kesters would be all right and she would be all right because she's in the pub with a bit of all right. YES SHE IS.

She's sure that lad over there's one of Kester's mates. Going to go across though it'll be a circus getting off this high seat. Knew it, she's rattled the table, everyone's looking. Head down, lets the blushes fall off her face and into the carpet where she can press them in with her bouncy tread.

"Sorry to bother you, but you haven't seen Kester Dean tonight?"

"Nah, ain't seen him." He's calling to some other lad at the fruit machine. "Yo, blud, seen Kes? Kester Dean?"

The lad turns, shakes his head. "Nah, man."

Back at the high seat knowing the best way to take it now, five foot one and up on the thing just like that. Oh shit, needs to wad up, better wait for Cliff to get back so he knows where she is. *Cliff*, hmm, not feeling the name, why couldn't he be called Ronnie, something good.

Here, he's coming. Smile, pat the table. "Lovely."

Drinks put down, his does a tiny slop. Oh, and the jacket's coming off. She likes his T-shirt. It's plain but she likes it, dark green, not too tight. Look at him going for his pint there, phwoar, that's a feeling not a word, that is, what a reaching forearm he's got, it's just the right size and shape. Name tattooed on the inside of it, no skimping on ink. LEAH running down to his big palm, same with the other arm, except it's LEWIS. The kids, aw.

"So, isn't this nice, Jean Jeanie?" He's standing and she's sitting and it is, it is so very nice.

"It is nice, Cliff, aye." Feeling seventeen, the old accent's thickened to what it once was. Needs to remember herself now. Tastes her gin and tonic. Appreciates the zinged-up tongue. Bit awkward, so's he, but good awkward. Quiver, spasm, flutter, and that's just her. Look about and show nothing, Jeanie.

"Located the whereabouts yet?"

"Yer what?"

"Son?"

"No, wish I had, can't exactly chill."

"Text him. Say yer got some fantastic news. He'll get back. Natural curiosity."

"Got no fantastic news, nothing he'd think was fantastic."

"Don't matter."

"He'll be disappointed I haven't won the rollover."

"So what. You're disappointed he ain't been in touch."

"True." She's smiling, naughty, shaking her puffer hanging on the back of the seat, trying to find out where she's stuffed her phone.

"You've lost something."

"What?"

"Something's fallen out yer jacket."

"Where?"

"There."

She's twisting her neck from high up. Looking for her phone. Looking at the bloody carpet again. "Where?"

"*There.*"

"Ah, right."

"What is it?"

"That?"

"Yeah, that."

"That, er, it's my little potato peeler."

"Yer carry a knife?"

"No."

"No?"

"Well, yes, tonight."

"I'm not into that, Jean Jeanie."

"No, me neither."

"Yer were expecting to peel potatoes?" He's putting his jacket on. "Just need a cigarette."

"Shall I come?"

"No, stay in the warm." Picking up the knife, giving it to her.

"Ta." Putting it away in her puffer. "I wasn't, I mean, I wouldn't, God, I'm not into knives, the opposite."

Nods. "Won't be long."

She looks after him for a second, then finds her phone. Opportunity to send that I've-some-fantastic-news message to Kester. One-off ploy, this. If he falls for it tonight, he'll be wise to it tomorrow. There. Done. Sent. PS in her mind: Please let me know if you're all right, Kes. I want to kick back with this man I've met, Cliff. He's a smoker but I think he could be the one.

Can't go to the toilet, people looking for seats, like gold dust, these. She'd be happy standing but don't want to leave these drinks on the table, those two raucous chatters leaning on the pillar behind her will close in while she's away and land spittle in her gin. Have to hang on. He won't be long. Shaking her head, keeping the bottom lip inside her mouth with her top teeth. Fancy that knife falling on the carpet like that. Could only happen to her. Wait till she tells Irwin. If yer had a brain yer'd be dangerous, he'll say. Going to be interesting to see how he takes it, her having a boyfriend, possibly a live-in partner. Kester, he'll be stumped. Mum got herself a man.

How to kill time? She'll do a bit of people-watching, a bit of back-of-throat humming. Wonders if he'll try kissing her at some point. She hopes it goes well. It'll go better than well. Can already taste it.

What does he call Won't Be Long? Don't get his Won't Be Long. Ten mins max she'd call Won't Be Long. Only got gin because she's sipping it with a mouth like a urethra. Saw one on the telly. She could get a half in for them both. He's a half still to go at. A fiver'd cover it, here. What if he don't come back? He's not coming back, is he? He's gone. She puts her puffer jacket on, feels the knife, hard, inside it. What must it have looked like?

Jumping off the seat. Got her bouncy tread to fall back on. Aw, still. She did like him. Really liked him.

Freezing out. This coat's been worth it. No sign. Didn't think there would be. Can't lie. Gutted. Walking home, trying to be up. A surprise, how good-looking the High Road is on a night out, full of real dark and real light from the moon but the rest of it is electric or whatever. There's her phone going. Phone, phone, phone, found the knife, phone, phone, phone, found the phone.

Don't recognise the number. "Hello?"

"Hello, is that, erm, *Jeanie?*"

"Me, aye."

"Hi there, I'm one of the staff nurses at the emergency department at St Helier's."

Heart's punching its way out of her. "No!"

"Jeanie?"

"Is he all right?"

"You've heard?"

"Heard what?" She's screaming. "Tell me, tell me, please, just tell me."

"Sorry, I know this is –"

Crying, screaming. "Say it."

"There was an incident. He sustained an injury, was brought in as an emergency. He's in surgery at the moment."

On her knees, no, no, no, get up, get up, running. She's running now. "Tell him Mummy's coming."

"He's in surgery. Sorry, I'm a bit confused. He has you in his phone as emergency contact. He has a mum?"

"What the fuck yer saying?"

"Right, OK, I'm ringing to let you know Irwin, *Irwin Peake*, has been brought in with a serious injury."

She stops running. "Irwin has? How? Why?"

"Knife trauma. I really can't say much over the phone. We'll get one of the doctors to have a word with you when you get here. I think a policeman's still around somewhere too. Is there anyone else who should be informed?"

"No. Well, that's for Irwin to say. He went down to complain about the noise, didn't he?"

"Sorry, I don't have any details. Best speak to the police."

Running, she's running again. "He'll be all right, won't he?"

"For now, just focus on getting here. Safely."

Phone back in pocket. Irwin, why'd yer go down there for? Irwin, where the hell am I going? Phone out of pocket. Google Maps. An hour forty on foot. Need to turn around as well. Giving it everything in the wrong direction. She's got this. Will run until she gets there even though she don't want to get there because getting there's harder than this.

Need to run the idiot off yer, darl. She can hear him now. And she's still running, pushing on, trying to find her way, the wet red spread between her legs making its own map.

Running to a round-and-round door that won't go round right into the warm and light and she will speak. When she can. Fit to drop. Nurse taking her into a room, nice room, must be a bad-news room. Nurse asking her to sit down but she can't sit down until she's tied her puffer round her waist. Nurse gone to get her a coffee. Doctor coming. Doctor's here. He's dead. Irwin's dead. Flat blue NHS carpet. See the sea. It's not normally this calm. Is that her phone? It is. Word from Kester: Madting! Well lit! You won on the scratchcards or what?!!!

FICTION

DREAMING POSSIBILITY

ELIZABETH BAINES

The storm has reached us from the north. I stand at the window and watch the fence at the end of the field vacuumed back towards the sea and then flung inland towards the house. The grey sky seethes.

The baby needs feeding, my mother is saying behind me. She has picked him up and holds him out to me in his white fluffy swaddling, the shawl she knitted, sitting here by the fire, serene in her house and in her sense of the onward progression of the generations, the steady continuation of the world as she knows it.

The baby's mouth is opening like that of a fish, he's a fish in the air, his raw primordial fingers worrying the wool.

I don't meet her eye as I take him, though I know she is peering at me keenly. I know what she thinks: that I need care. That she has a double burden: not just the baby, born here in her house, but a daughter unable to rejoice or accept her new role with grace and equanimity.

Postnatal depression, she calls it. That's the cause she finds this time for the lifelong trouble with her daughter. A new name to tuck it under. Another explanation, with another implication that it's temporary, the effect this time of hormones that will ebb away. Things will always get better. That's my mother, in spite of all the evidence.

I sit with the baby beside the fire. A dragon's breath comes down the chimney, fluttering and flattening the flames. Overhead, something knocks on the roof.

My mother says, hovering: I'm sure Abe will get here soon. For my mother, that's another explanation: Abe's non-arrival from the north. The fact that my partner, the baby's father, hasn't rung and isn't answering my calls or texts.

I lift my top, soggy with milk, my body responding to the baby's coughing sounds, propelled, irrespective of me, by nature's imperative.

The baby clamps on with his animal instinct, his jaws strong enough to send a momentary pain, the foot of his frog-leg pressed on my stomach. Such a fierce will to live. Such a fragile being.

The thought comes to me of the frog I impaled on my garden fork this time last year, in a much calmer February, when I had my own garden, before the seed of this child took root in my belly against all the odds – my age, and the fact that by then Abe and I hardly ever slept together.

I had seen the frog earlier as I gardened. There it was when I lifted a clump of leaves, in trusting hibernating sleep, exposed to the cold and to careless hands like my own. I picked it up and put it into the safety of creepers nearby. It must have woken. Deep in the slowed blood of its veins some reflex warning of danger must have been triggered and travelled to those concertinaed limbs. The limbs unfolded and flexed and took it deeper into the weeds. Five minutes later, I plunged in my fork, and the fork came up with the frog impaled on a tine, its legs flailing, nature battling in vain against the fate I had unwittingly imposed.

The insects I crushed, without a thought, as a child. The ants, a whole ordered civilisation, tracing their route over the garden path. I had seen my mother use a boiling kettle on an ants' nest, so I tipped a cup of piping-hot water onto their procession and watched them die – their toffee-coloured bodies curling, those that had escaped running in panicked apocalyptic circles.

It was then that I started having the flooding dreams. Dreams of water creeping towards you stealthy but fast, while your back was turned, and when you ran to escape it there was no escape after all: it had been creeping too from the other direction. And soon there was nothing but silver water on all sides, deadly smooth as far as the eye could see.

I would wake in panic, but the dream still swilled my limbs, the darkness rippled over my mouth and nose and wide-open eyes. I cried out. They had to get me a night light. But the walls I could see now seemed to move towards me, encroaching like the sea. I would gasp, I couldn't breathe ...

The name they had for it then was Anxiety Disorder. Was I eating, was I sleeping? the Child Psychiatrist asked my burdened parents. That too, it was decided, could be due to some hormonal imbalance, a lack of serotonin maybe, to be corrected with a drug. Though the drug did not correct the feelings, that sudden sense, as I played on the beach with the other kids, of things going wrong. The way that the sight of a piece of plastic caught in the reeds, or a factory chimney belching smoke, would make me stop on the spot, transfixed by a sense of spoliation and dread.

They dropped that label as I grew, and found another, better for them: Moody Teenager. They tried to josh me out of it, and when that didn't work they mocked me, and when that made me even more miserable they were annoyed. They began to suspect it was a matter of choice – I *chose* to be moody. Besides, they had problems of their own.

And there, in my twenties, was another explanation, dug up by a counsellor and handed over like a prize: a childhood of tension caused by sensing the discord between my parents that they worked hard to hide.

My mother brings a cup of tea and places it beside me at the fire. She's making sure I keep my fluid intake up, to keep the breast milk flowing, helping me through the conscientious postnatal rituals. The baby has finished feeding. His mouth slackens, drops away, milk leaking along his cheek and down my breast. His face reddens, and beneath my hand I feel his nappy fill, a huge and forceful eruption out of such a tiny shrimp of a thing.

A sigh escapes me. I force my heavy limbs to move me out of the chair to the changing mat, and begin the wearying task of unbuttoning his sleepsuit, sodden and yellow at the back, right up to the shoulder blades, where the shit was propelled out of the nappy. I lever out his amphibian legs and peel the stinking mess away.

Outside, something flies past the window and then clatters across the yard at the side of the house. The wind is howling in the chimney now.

My mother switches on the TV, replays the pictures of the storm in the north, the trees across the roads, the overhead lines down, the coastal railway tracks washed into the sea.

I'm sure Abe will get through, she says, he would have left before it got so bad. She is working on convincing me, working on convincing herself.

I nod. There's no point in doing anything else. She'd be far too upset if things between me and Abe are not what she would want them to be, she with her happy-ever-after mentality, she who had an unhappy marriage to my father but would never admit it even to herself, at the time or, especially, now, now that my father's dead. He can exist in sanitised memory, no longer here to disprove the mythology she has built around their marriage. She whose walls are decked with images of a world she wants to believe is still the norm – country lanes overflowing with flowers not yet endangered, peaceful and quaint, with an air of having always been so and destined always to be. All in spite of the evidence in front of her eyes, at the end of her own field.

I leave the changed baby kicking on his mat and go to the window and look out at the field. Just beyond the battling fence at its end, where the ground dips immediately to rocks and sand, there was once a grassy bank, dotted with primroses in spring, and a hundred-metre walk to the beach.

It is my mother who must be protected, it is *I* who must bear the burden of protecting *her*, from the truths she can't face. She would like to believe that the baby has brought me and Abe together. She would like to believe that there was never much wrong. And what she wants to believe, she does. She believes he's my saviour. She has no idea that the very thing that makes him so for her is the very thing that has driven me from him. The solicitude. The hand on my back propelling me towards sofas and chairs. The urging to see a counsellor again. All because I told him my dreams. Because I confided the vision I had, that time we were on holiday, crossing Lake Como.

There was hardly a breeze as we crossed. The boat cut through a deep-turquoise mirror that reflected at its far edge a pyramid of red roofs on the shore, caught in a classic, time-honoured scene, central to Western art and civilisation. A young couple with a baby stood nearby, very close to the rails. The mother held the baby loosely. The water slicked below. The baby's head swung near the rails. And I saw it. I saw the baby slip from the woman's grasp and plummet over the side, I saw the blue water fold over its nostrils and mouth, and then the baby disappeared as the water went on implacably flowing.

I blinked. The couple were moving off with their baby. I had to sit down. I was trembling. I vomited.

You need to see a counsellor, Abe said after I told him. Sweetheart. Darling. All concern, all empathy, desperate to help. Yes, you need to see a counsellor, my mother said. They were agreed, they agreed it together. Without any ill intent, they were in a conspiracy against me, a conspiracy to condemn as pathological the sense of the constant undercurrent of awful possibility.

My mother, I know, finds it hard to match my overconcern for that baby of strangers with my lack of joy in my own. Only madness, a wrong wire in the brain, or the chemical slip of postnatal depression, can explain it. Or Abe's absence, or, of course, the ruin of our home, my mother's idea of a woman's first priority.

In the autumn in the north there were days of incessant rain, drumming on our skylight and the glass conservatory roof. Water began to spout like Delphic fountains from the drains. Soon we were wading on the street, and very soon after, the road was impassable, a raging torrent. And then the mountain behind the house came sliding down.

Next day the countryside around was the silver panorama of my dreams, a scene that had lurked all my life in the coils of my brain and the cells of the blood coursing in my veins.

It was Abe, not I, who was shocked.

I heard him talking to my mother when we got here, to the coast. *Numb*, I heard him say, describing how I was at the refuge centre. *Almost catatonic.*

Text him again, says my mother behind me. She has picked up the baby, wrapped him in his sleeper and put him in the pram.

Outside the wind finally takes the fence. It rises up, an undulating wooden snake, then veers to the left and out of sight.

My phone has no signal. I go upstairs to see if I can get one there.

The landing reverberates with the clattering sound of the wind catching the roof tiles.

Still no signal on my phone.

Nothing, I tell my mother, coming back downstairs, and just at that moment the lights flicker off and the TV goes blank.

Later, in the quiet after the storm, we find our way around in candlelight. My mother is fretting over her lost fence, but is filled with a happy satisfaction: we have heard from Abe. He never set out. He stayed in the northern office to weather the storm.

With a girl-guide, sleepover jollity, my mother makes cocoa and brings it over to the fire.

She pats my arm with affectionate instruction: *It was only a passing storm. Everything's fine.*

Later still, in the early hours, I am woken by a sound I have never heard before and have never imagined: a hollow unbroken roar. I sit up, thinking of fire, and turn on the light. The noise surrounds me, fills the room, seeming to come from the walls. I get up and open the bedroom door. The sound is here, too, on the landing, the sound of pressure emanating, it seems, from the fabric of the house. Yet my mother is undisturbed, no light is showing beneath her door. Is the sound in my head?

I go back to my room and pull open the curtain. Dawn is beginning. There's a line of light in the east by which I can see that the ocean is striated with white all the way to the horizon, the waves whipped up by the steady implacable wind funnelling through the shell of this house.

Beside the bed the baby in his cot begins to squirm and make his coughing sounds. I lift him out. He is quiet as I undo my top to feed him, this child who may or may not survive the collapsing certainties of this world. His dark-blue eyes meet mine with a steady gaze. The milk floods in.

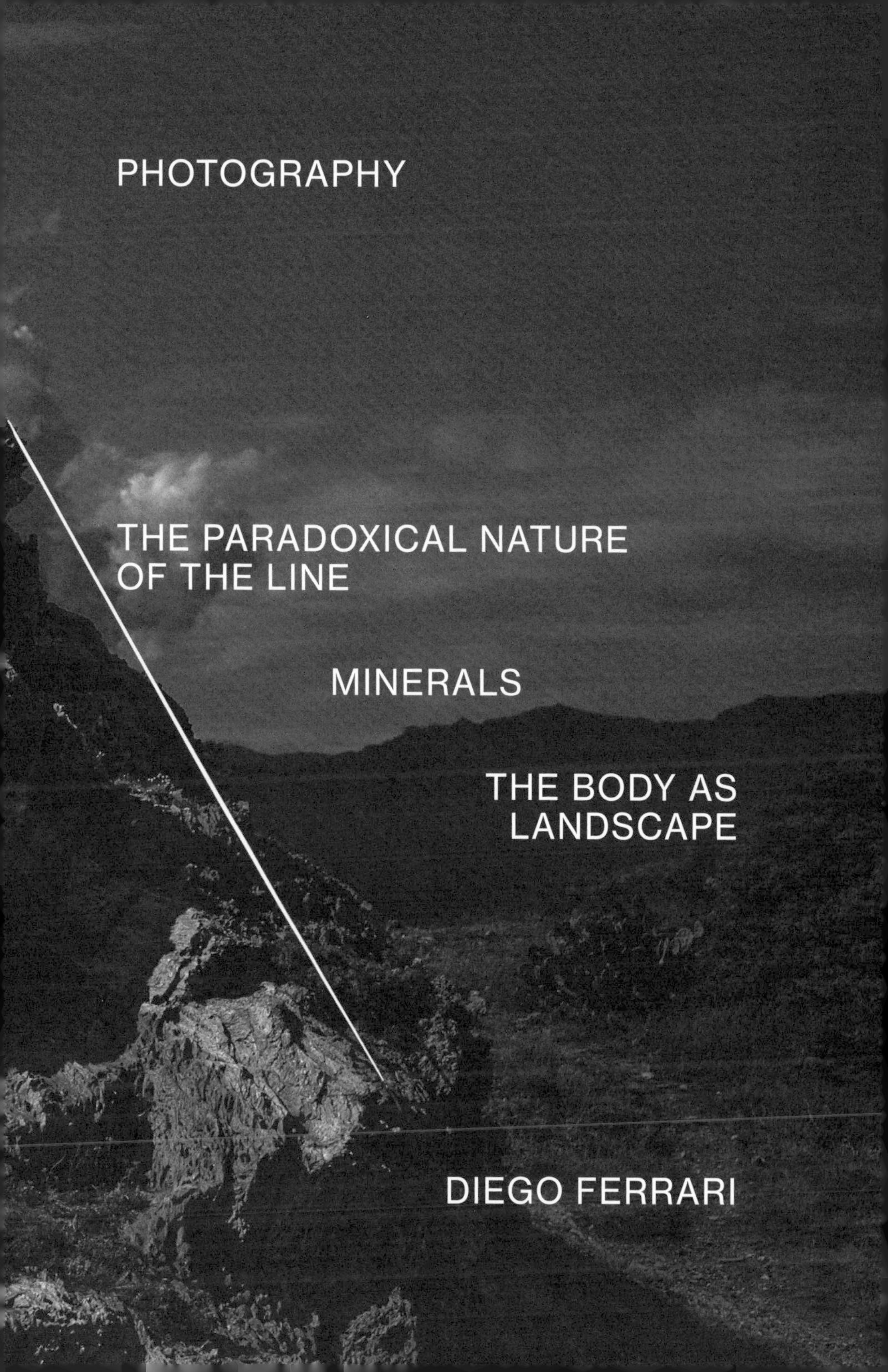

PHOTOGRAPHY

THE PARADOXICAL NATURE
OF THE LINE

MINERALS

THE BODY AS
LANDSCAPE

DIEGO FERRARI

These three bodies of work are inspired by the Cap de Creus peninsula in Catalunya, northern Spain. Cap de Creus is fascinating for its geomorphology and a wild, almost treeless landscape, sculpted by the fierce tramontana wind and criss-crossed by streams of pegmatitic lava in which seams of schist, tourmaline and feldspar are visible, depending on the angle of the sun. The natural environment is a living entity, separate from human consciousness. We read landscapes through linearities, symmetries and shapes, looking for a way to measure the power of the land against our human dimensions. Immanuel Kant theorised the mathematical sublime, exploring how our feelings of awe and wonder in landscape are linked to scale, magnitude and, ultimately, to infinity. The line represents our impact on the land as much as the dimensionality of the landscape and its mineral integrity. We perceive the world through the body. In these images, bodies act as mirrors, reflecting the light of the sun, obliterating themselves in the process, dissolving into the landscape. These performative acts unite the body and the landscape, as does the line, which is drawn physically on the landscape, not added digitally. Through performance as an act of perception, the images present us with a relational path to the sublime within nature.

Diego Ferrari and Jean McNeil

The Paradoxical Nature of the Line, May 2019–ongoing

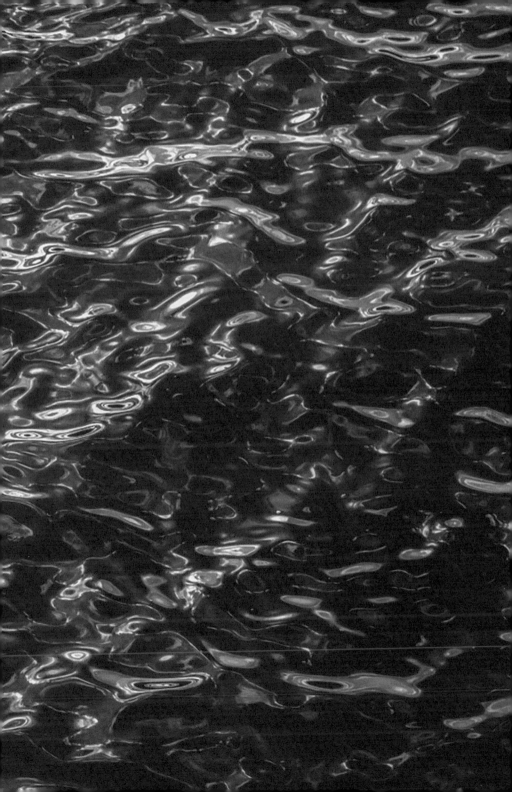

Minerals, Cap de Creus – Earth, Air and Water, 2017–2018

The Body as Landscape – Luminosity, 2018–ongoing

POETRY

SARAH BARR
LAURA LEWIS-WATERS
M. W. BEWICK

SWANS ON THE VLTAVA RIVER

SARAH BARR

December, and we tramp over snow-crusted cobbles
from our downtown hotel next to the little park
and walk a mile by the river.

Before we cross the bridge,
they appear as I've heard they do,
as if they've flown in while we were looking the other way,

too many to count in the twilight,
now silent on the dark, glistening water,
twenty, thirty, or more, a gathering of white,
their feathery curves, folded wings,
and their glances: bold, secretive,
as if they're in disguise
and there's something they could tell us
before they set off.

TIANLIN

LAURA LEWIS-WATERS

parched paddy
green bursts
gr ound water
desert des ert
deserted cracks
    desertified
village dis(appear)

The poem was inspired by a photograph in the Independent
*of disappearing rice paddies. Tianlin, in southern China, is
just one of many places where climate change is reducing
groundwater, resulting in parched paddies and, consequently,
famine and poverty.*

THE FORCE OF A LEAF

M. W. BEWICK

The skeleton leaf you found on the trail,
free of the mulch of the early year.
Lucky, you said, not to be caught in the grip
of boot or bike tyre, paw or hoof.
Gossamer is too slight a word, I thought,
as you held it up to the darkening sky.
No silk, no cotton, no lace, no veil,
no golden illumination of its filigree grace.
The leaf is a cold gate of wrought iron,
creaking as you heave it for entry.
The leaf shudders but closes you out.
The winter is its rusted hinge.
The leaf does not want you,
does not want to know.
Force yourself upon this leaf,
it will mark your hands
                          red as blood

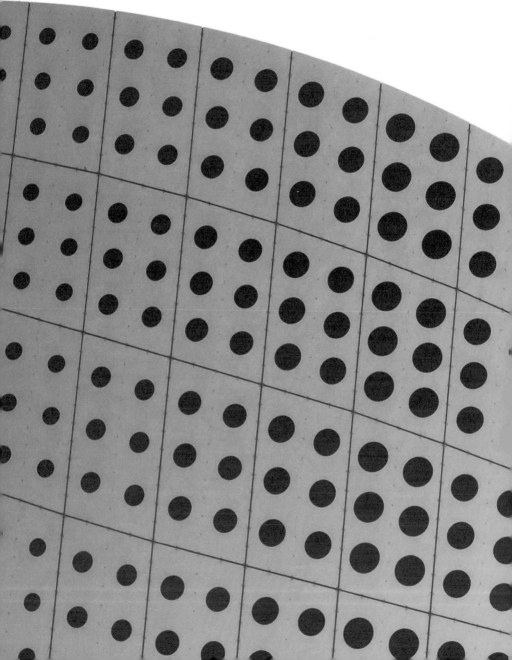

FICTION

BETTER PEOPLE

REENA DENNHARDT

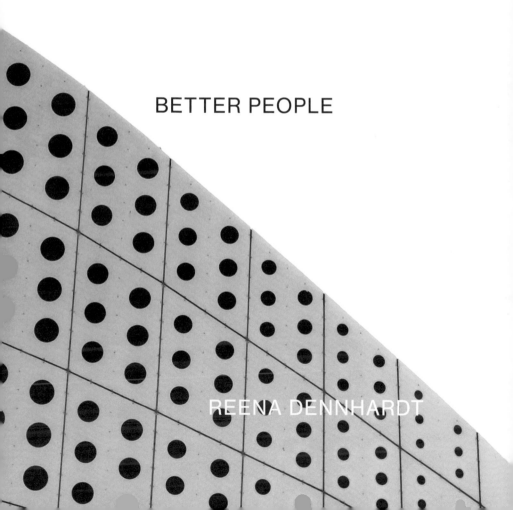

The air in here is too hot, but the prickle of sweat on my skin is telling me that I am still alive. Just. No more than just. Beside me, Olaf, my living child, is shivering like an animal without fur. My body wants to tell him he isn't alone, because my mouth can't. I pull him towards me and sit as still as I can.

Through the chasm of this waiting room, I hear his breath syncing with the creak of my ribcage. I worry firstly that he is frightened, and secondly that he is frightened of me. Then footsteps click towards us. I think they will take Olaf with them and away from me. They walk in with grinning faces and a toy kangaroo for my son. But their smiles don't reach their eyes. Seeing this sends a violent, thumping fear through me. I'm deafened by it. Deaf to both Olaf's crying and my own.

"Don't be afraid," I whisper, kneeling beside the people taking my seven-year-old. They won't let me touch him, prising him back when he reaches for me. "Please don't be afraid of anything. I love you."

No one answers. They won't talk to my face. I understand why; I couldn't look myself in the eye either.

"We'll be back. Soonish," says a voice through the closing door. "Is there anything you need?"

I pound fists against a door that isn't even locked. I whisper my children's names between sobs. I know I should be strong but can't keep myself from falling the fuck apart; losing two children in one day is too much.

Soonish, as it happens, is very soon and I shuffle out with escorts. I concentrate on walking through the kind of cramp that follows long periods of sitting, down the dim corridors of the building we call MISSY. The Ministry of Information Supra Security is famous, not least for its round windows. Some call this The House of a Thousand Eyes; others, more prosaically, a Thousand Arseholes.

They take me into a room that is mainly glass and I blink furiously. I haven't seen natural light for three meals, which could be one day or three or six. It's hard to tell. A suited man is waiting: Jay. His movements seem deliberately slow and tell me

Jay won't rush for anyone. He is a man who knows the world will wait for him, even when it can't afford to.

Twenty chairs lap the table. Jay pours water for the two of us, sips languidly.

An aquarium wall separates us from staff whose sideways glances slip in as they walk past. I look at the ceiling, the floor and then out of the window. Like all the windows of this building it is strangely unspotted, completely free of the grimy rain that normally stains everything around here. The view takes my mind outside; we don't have views this spectacular back home and I hope Olaf is looking too. I hope seeing it makes him remember the shiny-cheeked feeling after a day by the sea.

Jay looks at me. I smile quickly; a tic that is immune to the tragedy of my circumstances. He smiles back. He looks at ease here, like a man made for this room. His brown hair blends into the one wood-panelled wall, which is behind him, and from certain angles, the light reflects just so and gives his head a strange halo effect. He helps himself to a strawberry, and gestures that I should too. I shake my head. This doesn't feel like a moment to experiment; strawberries are an unheard-of luxury nowadays, rare and expensive. I've certainly never had one. He tosses the ends of his tightly knotted necktie over his shoulder and takes a juicy bite.

The air-conditioning system is intermittently blasting nauseating heat or extreme cold, which takes the boardroom from tundra to tropical and back again in seconds. It feels like time-travel, but I say nothing, holding my breath as the hairs on my arms stand and fall. Jay runs his fingers over the table and his eyes tell me that he expects me to begin. But I don't, because I don't know where to.

Then Jay speaks, in a voice that is low and soft, a voice that is in on secrets. He tells me Olaf is fine.

Looking around, I realise I'm sitting in a vortex of photos. The sideboard is decked with them, frames packed together tightly, applauding the life this man across the table has lived. The display cements his reputation as Mr Good Guy, smiling out from Condé Nast slums and Disney disasters. My breathing quickens. We sit opposite each other for a few minutes. Our silence is loud. Then he slides over a photo of Carmen.

"Isn't she beautiful," I say, unable to take my eyes off my child, touching her face with my greedy fingertips.

"Was," he says. "Was beautiful."

I can't do more than nod. Carmen was floaty and light, and I don't want to imagine her dead. In my head, she is a butterfly-child, flitting around restlessly, even before she could walk.

"She drowned," he says.

My howl sounds too big for my body.

"We know what happened." His voice has wind chill. "Maternal negligence? A little flirty fun? The surveillance is clear."

A shaky film begins playing on the screen behind him. I see myself distracted by Kristo, instead of watching my kids, and I cover my face with my hands. Jay swipes on a second screen and live streams Olaf dressed as a blue kangaroo playing with other kangaroos. He looks happy.

My eyes flick nervously between the screen and the photo, unsure which child I should be observing. Jay snorts and switches the screens off. He smiles.

We'd spent the morning by the river. Olaf, Carmen and myself, knitting daisies and drawing pictures with grass. Until Kristo arrived and distracted me.

"One simple minute. Not even two. But it doesn't take more," Jay says, suddenly sympathetic.

"But she swam well."

"Fish swim well. Little girls less so."

"Can I see her? Where is she?"

"She could be halfway down the Atlantic by now. Unfortunately."

"I didn't let Carmen down on purpose."

"Down? Or drown?" He stares at me intently, then speaks in the most neutral tone imaginable. "What the world believes, and how you spend the rest of your life, are up to you."

Everything about him is self-congratulatory. He tells me his people could make sure no one thinks I just killed my own child.

"Gossip being what it is ..."

"I love my children." My voice is small, sounds as though it comes from someone else.

"Loved." He pours himself more water, drinks. He puts his glass down, leans over to tip a capsule of powder into mine. He picks up my limp wrist, pulls out one of my fingers and uses it to stir. Then pushes the cocktail towards me.

"Cyanide. Some say it tastes sweet." Jay sits back and crosses his legs. "A little electric Kool-Aid?"

I am too scared to scream. My heart begins to hurt.

"They also say life's never the same after you've lost a child. Maybe drinking this is better than losing both your children?" He leans forward again. "Or maybe you learn to accept that life does go on and you leave with Olaf, just bury the one today."

I am holding my cyanide finger away from my body, as far from my face as I can.

"What are you so afraid of?" He takes a sip of his clear water. "There's really nothing to be scared of because you have choices. The first is being cooperative. The second, uncooperative."

He knows I don't have a mother or father to look out for me. I can see it on his face. He knows being poor in these circumstances makes me someone else's property. Seeing me understand makes him smile.

"Ha ha, joke. It's vitamin C. Helps clarify your position on the subject of living."

He takes a mouthful to prove the solution in my glass won't kill me, swallows ostentatiously.

"Nothing to be afraid of," he repeats, but in a different voice. He takes a second taste, kisses his bunched-up fingers and parks the cloudy concoction in front of me.

I don't know how to react, so I don't.

"This isn't what you think it is," he says. "Informal Informing ..." He comes across as someone doing a normal day's work. It isn't like a spy movie; he isn't in uniform or even angry. His eyes have lost their hardness, look soft, kind. It's as if someone behind his face is speed-dealing a deck of emotions.

Informal Informers are the stuff of local lore. No one knows one. No one has ever met one. But everyone knows someone who has.

Jay leans in towards me, careful to stop his cufflinks scraping on the table. He picks another strawberry from the abundant display, pushes the bowl my way, and with a slow blink encourages me to eat. His mouth is now a wet, red slash, telling me about the fruit I don't want to taste. He talks about their versatility, their delicate balance of sweet and sour. He tells me they are easy to cultivate in small enclosed spaces.

"This is bribery," I say.

"If it was bribery" – he smiles – "you could say no."

My welcome to Informal Informing is quick and efficient: he tells me they'll be in touch when they need me; he tells me not to worry; he assures me no one will see me as the bad mother who killed her child.

"This system wouldn't work without the Informal Informers. Without people like you to guide others towards our light. You'll find you fit into our organisation well. And over time, you'll see that what we do is different from and better than what we are reputed to be doing." Jay downs the cloudy glass of vitamin C then takes it to the far end of the table and pours me a fresh glass of water.

When I don't drink it, he looks exasperated, waves someone over and gestures them to escort me out.

"We'll need to trust each other, if we want this to work." He shakes my hand.

Olaf and I leave the building. He looks clean, fed and, all things considered, too happy. When he tells me he likes his new friends and is looking forward to visiting again, I pull him closer.

"Don't worry," he whispers, skipping to keep up with my hurrying. "This is our secret."

I turn around in surprise and see him waving at someone in the building behind us. I stop, bend to hold him.

"We need to share more now …" I say. He is looking past me, not at me. I take his warm face in my cold hands. There's light in his eyes.

"Now that Carmen is gone," he says, still looking beyond me.

I fall to my knees and hug him hard.

*

That evening, we're back home and our neighbours have heard the bad news. They stand in our doorway, holding boxes of food that are meant to comfort. They apologise in calm voices then leave quickly because they know grief is personal.

My brother calls. I spend the days until he arrives in a daze, balled up small on myself. Olaf self-caters from the Tupperware mountain on our table, which makes me wonder why I am still here.

My brother takes Olaf places while I sit at home and wear myself out from the inside. Losing his sister has turned my son into the perfect child who will eat and sleep and speak like the adult he isn't meant to be. One day, when I FaceTime to order him home from the playground, I see him wave a suited grown-up goodbye.

"Who is that?" I ask.

"A teacher." He presses his lips together and I know he is lying to my face. Teachers don't wear cufflinks.

The need to hide doesn't leave me. Not when my brother disappears two weeks later. Not even when autumn becomes winter. The crying has ceased but the pain inside stays stubborn. Over time, I realise the days all hurt in different and accidental ways. They make the winter drag. I long for the lightness of spring and for seasons to matter again.

When I ask Olaf how he would like to remember his sister on her birthday, he shakes his head and leaves the flat, walking out of the door backwards as if I might hurt him. Later, when he returns, he has something that could be strawberry juice on his shirt. He tells me to invite Carmen's friends and to play her favourite music. He wants a ceremony in our living room where we can all talk about Carmen and close her Facebook account together.

"That's better than you spending the day remembering Carmen in your head and hating the world for not dying with her," says my eight-year-old son. "It's time for us to move on."

On Carmen's birthday, I expect loss to lacerate me, but the neighbours don't give grief a chance, appearing at the door ready to share hugs and detailed memories of the child we've all lost. They wear the bubblegum-pink clothing Carmen loved and carry plates of her favourite foods.

I smile for the first time in eight months, and feel the relief that comes with talking and not just thinking about Carmen. Once they leave, and it is just Olaf and myself, we cry. Quietly, differently, separately but together.

"There's so much good stuff to remember," says Olaf. "And nothing bad." He laughs suddenly, and for the first time it feels as if there is a way forward.

It is another innocuous April morning, halfway through a week of unusually high temperatures, when a box of strawberries appears on the doorstep. I put them on the table and stare at the fruit for a whole hour before Olaf wakes up.

He isn't much of a morning eater, but when I turn around with his breakfast bowl, he is scoffing with concentration.

"These are great," he says, unfolding a handful of hulls.

I close the box to protests, insist we discover which neighbour to thank before eating. Strawberries are a foodstuff I never buy and their presence feels odd in my home. I wonder where Olaf first tried them. He isn't much of a trier.

"Let's take today off." I smile. "Have a picnic somewhere. Steal some time."

He shakes his head, points at the fridge calendar and his ticket for the school trip to the butterfly park.

I smile again, but thinly. Butterflies were Carmen's obsession.

"The day after tomorrow," he promises, picking up his packed lunch, overnight bag and waving his way out of the door.

I peer out the window, waiting for Olaf to cross the road. The doorbell rings. I scan the room on my way to answer it, looking out for whatever it is that he has forgotten to take with him. Jay stands before me, pushes red tulips into my arms.

"You look much better," he says.

When he slides past, I taste his scent in my mouth: pine, matching shampoo and soap. Instead of sitting down, he offers me coffee, and busies himself in my kitchen.

"Do sit down." He pulls out a chair. "I bring good news."

He speaks without seeming particularly pleased. He offers me my own milk, pouring when I find myself unable to speak. He opens the fridge and takes out the box of strawberries, helping himself and nudging the box towards me.

"I understand," he says. "You don't trust me or want me here. But as a foot soldier, your duties are clear." He eats another strawberry. "So, let's get this over with."

I stay where I am.

"Duty is duty. A debt is a debt."

Silence.

"How's Olaf?"

Silence.

"You must have questions?"

Expressions, including evidence that they may once have existed, are rare on Jay's face. Then he breaks open a smile.

"You're afraid of something," he says. "I can't help you if I don't know what it is."

He is right. I am afraid of something.

"Sometimes it's easier the other way. What don't you want?"

"To be an Informal Informer."

"Bit late for that, darling. We've done the paperwork."

"I don't want to be a hero. National or local."

As I say this, his tutting suggests that he does.

"You're actually quite low in the hierarchy, barely register in the ranking."

"And what exactly am I meant to do?"

"Nothing bad. Remember how good it felt when you were miserable and your neighbours were here for you. It's time to repay the debt."

"With Tupperware and talk?"

"Exactly so."

He didn't say: "Your mission, should you choose to accept it ..." He said:

"Mr Penfold in 349 is unwell."

"Is this some cheap trick to –"

"Make you a more valuable member of society? How clever of you to guess." There is conviction in his face. "You're going to provide a little everyday kindness."

"Schlepping hot meals around isn't what Informal Informers do." I'd heard the rumours.

"We're not the Gestapo, this isn't the Stasi. Techniques move on. You've spent enough time in our offices to know we're legit, but your look says you're expecting tricks? That's because you don't know that ethics have become all the rage in our line of business." He stands, rinses his cup and places it in the dishwasher.

"The only real question is whether you're going to do the right thing well or badly?"

His eyes land on the drawer I can't face opening. It's stuffed with empty plastic containers.

"I'm not asking you to put a gun to his head and shoot him. How can making a sick man dinner and caring a little be bad?"

I raise an eyebrow. Jay smiles too hard. He opens the drawer full of other people's Tupperware. Then he slumps theatrically and begins to expound. He rearranges my drawer as he talks.

"We have the Internet to monitor every aspect of everyone's life. In any given moment, we know what you are thinking and how you all feel. We've even become good at guessing what you are about to do, say and think next. But ..." Jays voice trails off, audibly irritated. He leans back to examine how much better the drawer looks when containers are fitted into one another by size and shape. "But ... we're having difficulty convincing our people we know them better than they know themselves. They don't believe us when we tell them what they really thought, or when we insist that what we think they're thinking is far superior to what they themselves think they're thinking. Or, indeed, are about to think." He stops talking, but keeps rotating his hands. "And we feel we're too far away. We want to be felt. You understand? We want to be like the weather, ever present in glorious technicolour."

He salutes, and sees himself out.

A cardboard box arrives on my doorstep the next morning. Inside, a laminated card for Recipe #349, ingredients which have been labelled, weighed and chopped.

At 12:30, I ring Mr Penfold's doorbell with a plate of hot lunch.

"Push," says a voice. No one leaves their door open in this neighbourhood. I walk in and wince at the smell of sickness.

Mr Penfold's face has a glassy glaze. His eyes look matt, and seem oblivious to the book in his lap.

He lifts the cover off the plate. "My favourite. How did you know?"

His chins are soft and undulate gently as he sits up to eat. I bring him cutlery, refill the water by his bed.

"I find people kind around here." His demeanour is gentle and we discuss the world in an optimistic way that makes me want to be a part of it.

The next morning another cardboard box on my doorstep contains ingredients, and a recipe for three. A handwritten note tells me Olaf will love it.

My son is standing in the kitchen when I come back from Mr Penfold's.

"You're smiling more." He jumps up for a hug. He smells like he always smells – wonderful. His warmth hugs my heart. "On the inside too." He picks up a spoon and goes for the pasta bake.

"Mr Penfold wants more."

"I like your new cooking. It's better than school."

It's the first time he has ever praised my cooking. I take an exaggerated bow. Life feels fuller as I watch him eat.

Within a week, the daily box and the list of people I deliver to has increased to ten. I like them all, and am starting to feel like a special kind of faithful person.

One of my wards has a son who wears nothing but black. Even his dog is black. I've passed him drinking beer with his mates late at night, a gang of hooded all-blacks.

The woman, Mrs Zucker, seems like a good person. She avoids confrontation with her only child by living around him. She's broken her leg, and the flat smells of her iodine gauzes and his cigarettes, but is otherwise immaculate.

I almost forget about Jay until three weeks later, he turns up.

"Congratulations," he says. "You've done well on hearts and minds."

I grin because praise feels good.

"We're glad you aren't lonely any more."

"I've never thought of myself as lonely."

"No one does. But that doesn't mean you weren't. It's the biggest killer, you know. Nowadays. Deadlier than fat, salt or cholesterol."

I wish this conversation would stop.

"You see how a small thing like a hot lunch can make a person happy?"

I nod.

"And you see how a small negative thing, like too much salt, the wrong recipe, or a little 'Kristraction' can ruin everything?" Jay's smile is ironic and oozes impunity. It gives me brain-shudders.

Jay leans in.

"As I've told you, we need you to be like the weather: constantly rearranging the world. Picture the wind blowing leaves and building dunes. Or rain forming rivers then cutting through stone. Imagine snow silencing and bloating the world. Or sun turning the sunflowers. We need you to change the landscape constantly, sometimes in indiscernible ways."

I lean back and straighten my arms.

"Your clients don't get out much. So, you need to bring change to them." Jay stands. "You do it like this." He smooths the back of the sofa, then drags it towards him. He turns to the wall, picks up Carmen's photo and swaps it into another frame. "Relocate your client's possessions by three centimetres. Never more. It's important to be consistent and minimal. Nudge a little every day and never more than once. Remember we are careful. We never presume."

He knows I've upped the ante, and sometimes visit my friends twice a day. He knows I'm getting off on gratitude over coffee and biscuits.

I've read about *Zersetzung*, know it makes life feel strange and uncomfortable – a living nightmare. I voice concerns.

"Your knowledge of the KGB and the Stasi is impressive, but remember they used this technique to instil fear. We aren't sucker-punching people into obedience. We're seducing them into happiness with well-chosen meals and friendships. We're keeping their lives interesting, normal."

The expression on his face isn't menacing. Instead, he stares at me with that dewy-eyed look which often accompanies benevolence.

"You'll find your actions have a broadening impact on your clients. We're making the world a better place."

My open-plan kitchen feels small and airless. I open a window. He turns on the fan.

"There isn't another way?"

"To learn that change is normal? You need to get them to a point where they are waiting for something to change and can no longer pretend nothing's bothering them."

"How will they feel?" I ask in a dubious voice.

"Strange," he says. "But also, strangely alive. Regular life is a well-defined but dynamic concept. People adapt when they have to. Evolution makes us who we are. Evolving makes people feel better."

It feels cooler once Jay's left, and pleasantly quiet.

I look around. My daughter's stuff is still sitting silently all over the flat. I push the sofa forward, put Carmen back in her place, feel the room regain normal proportions.

"I like you," says Mrs Zucker the next day. "Most people drain my energy. But it's nice having you around. You somehow know exactly what I want to eat and how I like it cooked. My son likes you too, I can tell."

Mrs Zucker's son nods slightly when I walk past him in the corridors now. I've seen him kicking a football about with Olaf, but his dark clothes and demeanour still unnerve me. I have the feeling their friendship could turn quickly.

When she goes to the bathroom, I move a few books around the bookshelves. A few days later, I move the dining table three centimetres to the left. Over the course of a week, I shift a rug, swap two pictures out of their frames and into new ones, rearrange a couple of bedroom cupboards and pour perfume into the bathroom disinfectant to give it more layers of disgusting. I start smiling as I work. What started off feeling sneaky, now feels elvish.

I'm on my way home when Jay calls from the building's elevator. I join him reluctantly. The doors close tight.

"Have you noticed how helping people doesn't always make them like you? Sometimes you'll find it's quite the opposite. Take Mrs Zucker's son, Horatio."

We are standing so close I can see the hairs on his nose. It feels too close to talk, so I listen.

"There's nothing wrong with Horatio. Maybe just in the way he sees the world. Or maybe just in the way Horatio will make Olaf see the world," says Jay.

I realise I have forgotten what saying nothing feels like.

Jay hands me a data stick and tells me to leave it under Horatio Zucker's pillow.

"It's just pictures of Horatio being happy with his ex-lover, Ronaldo. Wouldn't it be nice to remind Horatio of the good times? And have you noticed how bad his room smells? Too much stale sweat and angst." He presses a bag of aerosols in my hand. "So, we've bottled up some Ronaldo." Jay looks delighted.

The spray cans are numbered. Ronaldo number 7 is a messy morning smell. Ronaldo 9 is late night and seductive. Ronaldo 13 is sporting strong. And so on, an aerosol a day to douse Horatio's life in.

"Aren't we good?" says Jay with an uncanny wink when the elevator door opens.

I walk out, glad for the fresh air. He whistles to catch my attention.

"Focus. OK? On Horatio. And there's a new mother in 784 who needs your help. I think you know how it feels to pretend you don't feel alone."

The box is bigger the next morning and contains strange Brazilian snacks in a clear plastic bag labelled *Horatio* and a soft toy labelled *#784*. I act as instructed, not thinking about what I am doing to Mrs Zucker's son.

Eight days later, Mrs Zucker tells me about Horatio. He'd stood by his bed last night, gesticulating wildly, his face angry and urgent, hands making open-close movements as he told her that someone was messing with him. He was like his father, she'd thought, sometimes powerfully angry, sometimes distant, unpredictable and broody. Later, he'd run out of his bedroom, retching violently, his eyes sad and wet. Then he'd rolled out into the night without his dog or phone.

His mother is sitting in the window of his bedroom hugging herself tightly as she tells me. Like me, she is shaking.

When I return home with Horatio's dog, Jay is waiting.

"You've had a shock. I think you need a drink." He reaches into a cabinet and pulls out a bottle of cognac I'd long forgotten about. Looking for and not finding glasses, he pours into two teacups and gives me one.

"I drove him away." I shiver as I speak.

"Aren't we the detective."

Fury fills my eyes with tears.

"Horatio wasn't like us, was he. He wasn't normal." Jay's tone is gentle. "I think it's the best thing for a bad character."

"He was different, not bad."

Jay doesn't react. He does not know how it feels to lose a child.

"Horatio wasn't keen on living here and the neighbourhood feels tidier without him. You did your best to make him belong."

There's a bad taste in my mouth. It's not a taste I want to share.

"I need you to take care of Mrs Zucker in these difficult times. And the baby in 784. That little girl's mother might not make it much longer. Mr Penfold is weeks away from dying so you need to be extra kind to him. And then all your other clients. You have to keep going for their sakes, more than your own."

He keeps his finger on the handle of his cognac cup but doesn't lift it. The words lie on the table between us.

"May I remind you that you don't get rich working for rich people but you do get good when you work for good people."

"Why?" I ask.

"Why make the world a better place? Why make it nicer for people like us who belong in places like this? Why move out of motherhood into middle management? Why make a difference?"

His mouth twists into a camera smile. His eyes flash angrily above it. In that moment, I know that unlike a serial rapist, he'll never leave me for dead in a back alley. I know that like the weather, there's no control. No way out.

"If you only live for you, then you'll be the only person who's sad when you die."

I seem to have run out of words.

After he leaves, I stay sitting for a long time, needing to be surrounded by photos of Carmen and Olaf. Their gappy smiles remind me of the things about myself I never want to forget. The things I need to hold on to. To glue in place.

FICTION

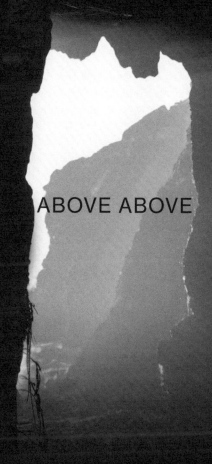

ABOVE ABOVE

JOSHUA SOUTHERN

Jad-da was deep down in the web of the Under-Tunuls. He was hunchd over a paticularlee thick clump of moss that he had uprootid, watchin a clustr of crawlurs fyting a much larjer creechur that Jad-da had not seen befaw. A long, twistin monstrositee with mor legs than all the uthr crawlurs put together. Taykin his charcol an payper, he began to mayk notes on the new speceemin. He new of no pryor naym for it, so he calld it menee-legs. He droo a kwik skech of the tynee beest, an jottid down how it moovd.

He had at furst ecspectid the menee-legs to win the battul, but as it curld arownd to byte at one of the crawlurs, the rest of them swarmd over it an began to attack its bodee. It rythd an tryd to shayk them off but they held firm, an evenchulee the menee-legs fell down, legs twiching as it dyed. He notid down this suprysin turn of events. The remayning crawlurs dug under its bodee an liftid it up onto their baks with a strenth for their small syze that impressd Jad-da. They began to carree it away. He reechd down an pluckd up the ded menee-legs, shayking off the crawlurs that still clung to their kill befaw they cud byte him. He wontid to see how it taystid.

His teef crunchd thru the shell, an with a pop its blud filld his mowth. The thing taystd lyk meet an moss, an od flayvr. Not bad, but not gud. He notid that down too, then, as an aftrthawt, smeerd a cornr of the payj with its blooish blud, to sho Nee-la wen he got home.

Nee-la did not lyk wen Jad-da caym down to the Under-Tunuls, but he was deetermind to do it, eevn if it ment ridiqoole from evreewon else in the Above. The uthrs did not lyk the Under-Tunuls eyther, an they did not lyk Jad-da for lyking the Under-Tunuls. Onlee the hunters went in, an onlee then a littl way for scavenjin, wen they hadnt cawt enuf fish for evreewon. But the fish wer runnin owt, they all new it, an stil they wud not leev the vast caverns of the Above, ware things wer warm an bryt. They refyusd to go down far enuf to fynd the amownt of food they needid.

He wud, tho. He wud ryt down all he cud of the Under-Tunuls so that he an Nee-la wud not hav to wuree abowt food eneemor. So theyd not hav to rely on the hunters. They cud provyd for themselves. The uthrs wudnt laff at him then. Not them, an not Bala. Bala hoo had tawt Jad-da as a boy, an scawnd him now as a man.

They all, even the hunters, did as Bala said, an Bala did not seem to care abowt a food shortij. All Bala cared abowt was his preshus barruls, big contayners of metul wich held the oyl to lyt fyres. Balas furst lessun to eech new jenerayshon of childrn was to be careful with the oyl. "Dont spill it. Dont drink it, no matter how thursty you may be. An most im-paw-tant-lee," he wud say, leening in clos to the frytend childrn, "dont ever, never, put fyre neer the barruls, or BOOM!" an he wud thro his hands owt, never fayling to mayk the yung ones jump. Long ago, wen he had been a chyld sat befaw Bala, Jad-da had stuck up his hand an askd wot wud happen wen the oyl ran owt. Bala had stud sylnt for a wyl, mowth flappin. In the end he just crackd him on the hed with his cayne an said nuthing. Bala didnt lyk kweschuns he cud not anser.

Down heer, in the Under-Tunuls, it was cold an dim an damp. Jad-da lykd the cold, it raysd bumps on his skin an mayd him feel mor aware, alyv. An he lykd the sownds too, the constant dripping an tapping. Wawter from the greyt layk that cuvrd the flor of the Above drippd down thru the dert, feedin the plants an creechurs that livd in the tunuls. The tunuls wer lit fayntlee by glowing clumps of moss that lynd the walls. Ly-ken, Bala calld it, tho he wud never say wy it glowd so. Bala claymd to no a lot, but there wer menee things it seemd to Jad-da that he cud not anser, not just abowt the ly-ken. Jad-da had tryd to ask him in the past abowt how the oyl mayd fyre, or how the big lyts mayd of glass an metul that lynd the walls of the Above werkd. His anser was always "Becos they do. Oyl mayks fyre an the fil-a-ments mayk lyt," wich didnt seem lyk a veree gud anser to Jad-da at all.

Jad-da had wons tryd to bring his mayt Nee-la down into the Under-Tunuls, but she wudnt go. Wen he sujestd it she shuk her hed an huddld closr to the fyrepit in the middl of their burrow. She lykd the fyre too much. She oftn askd him to stop, to leev the tunuls to the hunters. She had gotn mor insistnt since she had got the littl one insyd her. Now, she was eevn mor scared of him goin beelow. But he cudnt stop, nor did he wont to.

He was maykin his fynl notes on the menee-legs wen he herd a deep rumbling. It ekowd thru the tunul lyk the ror of a greyt beest. It was an angree, terifying sownd. The air hung still an he notisd for the furst tyme how stayle it was to breethe compaird to in the Above. His hands began to trembul, an so did the tunul. It wasnt just the flor that shuk, but the walls an roof, too. Wawter shuk free from the moss on the see-lin, falling in droplets arownd Jad-da, pattering agenst his fayc an nek an arms. His mynd turnd to the Above, to wot myt be happening in its vast caverns, to Nee-la, an the soon-to-be littl one, an he ran.

He lumberd along the tunul, grabbing handholds in the walls to pull him forwurd. The see-lin was low enuf that Jad-da had to crowch slytlee an in his rush he kept nocking his hed. Evreething shuk. The tunul trembuld. He wureed that the hol of the Under-Tunuls wer going to come down arownd him. Wurs, that the shayking myt bring down the walls an see-lin of the Above. He reechd for one of the rockee handls, fingertips scraypin agenst stown, almost compleetly taring one of his thick nayls off. He hissd an stuck the injurd fingers in his mowth an suckd but did not slow down. Tripping an skidding over rocks that had falln in the shayking he clamberd forwurd.

The flor of the tunul began to slowp upwerd, an Jad-da had to dig his fingers into the grownd to help him clym. At one poynt his feet slippd owt from under him an he fell hard on the grownd, byting his tung. The tayste of blud an dert filld his mowth. Spitting, he got bak up onto his hands an nees an continyood to clym. The glow of the moss behynd him faydid in the distance, leeving him in darkness.

He calld owt to Nee-la. He new it was poyntless, he was still far from home, but the thawt of her, alown, afrayd, overcaym him. He showtid her naym agen an agen as he crawld on. He showtid until his throwt was raw an it hurt too much to showt eneemor. All the wyl, the rumbling an shayking continyood, but he crawld ever onwerd. If he stoppd now, he wud never fynd Nee-la, an withowt Nee-la, wot was there?

He clamberd along lyk that for a wyl, til he cud heer voyces off in the distence. Showts ekowd down the tunuls. The shayking had gottn wurs, an he cud heer cracks an rumbls as stown browk an fell arownd him. A flickr of lyt apeerd in the distence, growing larjer as he got closr, an the walls of the tunul began to wyden. With the showts getting lowder an lowder, sheelding his eyes from the lyt that burnd after the total darkness, Jad-da stumbld owt of the Under-Tunuls an into the Above.

Most of the fil-a-ments heer had not browken, an the Above was still lit. The caverns wer pakd with peepl. Men an wimen ran too an fro, sum with childrn. Menee wer dyvin thru the cloth rags into the burrows that wer carvd in spyruls up the walls of the Above, ware they all livd. The saym activitee was goin on all thru the Above, mor peepl hurreein acros the stown brijis that connectid the hyer levuls of burrows. It was cayos. Jad-da saw no dyrekshun or purpos to their akshuns. There was noware they cud escayp the shayking, they wer simplee panikd to a frenzee. His burrow was on the uthr syd of the cavern, an there wer menee peepl between him an it.

"Nee-la? NEE-LA?"

He showtid her naym as he pushd thru the crowd. If he saw a fayc he recognysd, he grabbd them an askd if they had seen her. Most shuk their heds an pulld away, luking for peepl themselfs. Uthrs ignord him intyerly, not wontin to deel with an owtcast lyk him. He kursd them an moovd on.

He skirtid the baysin that held the greyt layk. A cupl of peepl had falln into the wawter an wer thrashin abowt, tryin to keep above the surfas. Lucklee, Jad-da was shurer on his feet than most, an he manijd to keep his balans. Uthrs wernt so luckee. A cupl mor peepl lost their footin an fell into the wawter. If eneebodee notisd, they didnt try to help.

Evenchulee, Jad-da mayd it thru the crowds. His burrow was almost dyrectlee above him, a few levuls up. Nee-la had to be insyd, he had seen no syn of her in the throng, but the rope laddr to the burrow was noware to be seen.

He groand an lukd arownd for sumthin to clym. A stak of emptee oyl barruls was lent agenst the wall. Jad-da pushd thru the throng of peepl still hurreeing abowt in a panik. He clamberd up onto the barruls, an jumpd from them onto a stown brij above. He ran along the brij until he stud beelow his burrow. One of the fil-a-ments protrudid from the wall just above him. He lept at it an grabbd on. Hoystin himself up onto the glass an metul cays of the fil-a-ment, he grabbd the bottum lej of the burrow an pulld himself into his home.

The burrow was dark. The fyrepit in the senter had gone owt. It tuk a moment for his eyes to ajust to the lack of lyt. The burrow was a mess. Pots lay browken in peeses all over the flor. The cot he had been chisiling for wen the bayb aryvd had crackd an split in too. Curld up in the far corner of the room, hands runnin protectivlee over her swolen belee, eyes wyde with feer an wet with teers, Nee-la lukd up at her mayt.

"Nee-la!" he cryd owt as he ran to her syd. She began to sob, an he rappd his arms arownd her. "Hush, hush. Is okay now. Is okay." He strokd her hair an held her clos.

"Jad-da ... wots happenin?" she manijd between sobs. "Wy is the wurld shaykin?" Her eyes wer wyld, an dartid arownd the burrow. He cud feel her tremblin.

"I dont no." He put a jentl hand on her stumak. "You okay? Both?"

He lukd her deep in the eyes, tryin to ree-ashur her. She swallowd an noddid. He smyld, then pulld her in an kissd her.

The tremblin got wurs suddnlee an Nee-la shreekd. The clay jar that held their oyl rashun toppld from its shelf, smashin on the flor an spillin oyl acros the room. Nee-la wayld an moovd to cleen it up, but Jad-da held her bak. The tremblin stoppd, as suddnlee as it had gottn wurs.

He turnd bak to Nee-la an helpd her up onto her feet. The faynt sownd of screems began to ekow in from the cavern. The mayts spun to fayc the entrans to their burrow, Nee-la pressin herself so clos to Jad-da that he cud feel her chest ryse an fall with her panikd breething. He tuk a step towards the entrans, but Nee-la wimperd an held him bak.

"Jad-da, dont. Not sayfe."

"I hav to, Nee-la. Wot if peepl need help?"

"They wudnt help you," she insistid.

"Its okay," he ashurd her. "I will be okay."

He pulld away an her grip on him loosnd. He paddid to the entrans, poking his hed owt from arownd the side of the rag. Evreewon had stoppd. Nobodee ran eneemor. They all stud perfectly still, all luking up towards the see-lin of the Above. Jad-da followd their gayze. At the veree hyest brij of the Above a groop of hunters wer stood in formayshun, speers an slings poyntid towards one of the elders burrows. Balas burrow. Jad-da pulld bak into his own home an turnd to Nee-la.

"Wot happend?" she said.

Jad-da shruggd. "Dont no." He poyntid upwerds. "Sumthin in Balas burrow. Sumthin rong. Will go see. Nee-la wayt, care for littl-one." Withowt anuthr werd, an befaw Nee-la cud protest, he duckd owt of the burrow an clamberd down onto the neerest brij. Jad-da clymd the rope laddrs from brij to brij, clymin hyer an hyer thru the Above, passin hundreds of peepl hoo mostlee stood starin at the topmost brij an Balas burrow.

Fynallee, he caym to the top brij. It was swarmin with elders an hunters. He mayd his way thru the crowd of peepl, ignorin the judjing luks of the elders as he passd by. He cud not see Bala eneeware. There was a larj gap between the hunters an Balas burrow. It seemd to Jad-da they wer afrayd to go neer. He pushd to the frunt of the pak of hunters, ware he was stoppd by a mus-q-lar feemale carreeing a long, sharp speer. Wen she reealysd hoo he was, she spat at his feet an raysd her speer at him.

"No entree, owtcast."

"Is okay, hunter. Let him pass."

The hunter spun as the cloth entrans to Balas burrow was pulld asyd. The peepl on the brij all tuk a step bak as a wayv of heet rushd thru them. Bala steppd owt onto the brij. The teechr lukd shaykn, an was drenchd in swet.

"But, teechr –"

Bala raysd a narld hand. "Kwyet, chyld. Let him pass."

The hunter noddid. She scowld at Jad-da, but steppd asyd. He followd Bala insyd.

Jad-da staggerd as he enterd the burrow, overwelmd by the increesing heet. Balas burrow was horriblee hot an horriblee bryt, so much so that he had to sheeld his eyes, tho not befaw notisin how much bigger Balas burrow was than enee uthr he had been in befaw.

"Bala? Bala, I cant see. Wot is happenin?"

Bala moovd forwurd an with tremblin fingers lowerd Jad-das hands from his eyes. He blinkd as the lyt blyndid him. Wen his syt returnd he could not beleev wot he saw. The bak wall of the burrow was gone. Browken to rubbl. There was a tunul behynd ware the wall had been. It slowpd up, an it was there that the lyt an heet wer coming from.

"Bala, I dont understand." His hands began to trembul as the teechrs did.

"Oh, Jad-da. I scawnd you. I feerd the Under-Tunuls, but you wer ryt to go down. I shud hav feerd the Above."

"Wot do you meen?"

"There is sumthing. Sumthing beyond. Sumthing above."

"Above?" he askd, confusd. "Bala, this is Above."

"No, chyld." Balas voyce was brayking. "Sumthing above the Above."

Jad-da stud sylent. The heet was almost unbareabl, but he cud not moov. He didnt understand. How cud sumthing egsist hyer than the Above? It wasnt possibl.

He tuk a step forwurd. Anuthr. Anuthr. Bala cryd owt to him, but he did not lissen to the teechr. He clymd over the rubbl, an into the tunul. The heet got wurs with eech step but he pushd on an into the lyt.

A land of fyre. Jad-da staggerd forwurd an fell to his nees. Fyre evreeware. It was evreeware an evreethin. Above it all, there was an orb of yello-wyt lyt. A burning, floting ball of fyre so immens that Jad-da thawt it was no wunder how the land burnd arownd him. The grownd was not the saym grayish-brown as the Above. It was almost red, similar to the rust that grew on the barruls of oyl. The land befaw him slowpd down until it was lost in a hayz of rust-cullerd dust. There wer no walls, at leest none that he cud see, it just kept going an going. It mayd the Above luk no bigger than one of the burrows.

There was a gasp behynd him. He lukd bak an saw Bala stumbl owt of the tunul. Arownd the tunul, the red rock an dert rose upwerds an upwerds into a poynt. Along the fayc of the rock wer cowntless pannuls of metul, reflectin the lyt of the fyre.

The floting orb burnd Jad-das eyes an scorchd him but he cud not luk away. He felt his skin crack an blister in the heet. Felt his mowth dry. His blud began to boyl. It was tuff to breethe. He thawt of Nee-la an their littl-one. Wot cud live in this fyre? Shurly nuthin cud survyv surrowndid by fyre? Bala mumbld sumthin Jad-da cud not heer. Teers streemd down his rinkuld cheeks, but dryd befaw they cud fall from his fayc. The teechr shuk his hed an collapsd. His payl skin was burning, flesh bubblin. His fayc pressd into the dert, eyes staring lyflesslee into nuthing.

Jad-da thawt onlee of Nee-la an the littl one. He moovd to the entrans an began to shift rock an bolder in frunt of the hole, ignorin how the hot stown seerd his hands. He had to plug it up. He had to protect them from the fyre, from the burning. It felt as if his flesh was meltin away.

It was too much. He fell to the grownd an cud not pick himself bak up. He tryd to reech for the hole, but his strenth was gone.

Sumthin shiftid in the rust-sand besyd him. A menee-legs pokd owt of the dert an crawld arownd. It did so for a wyl, then dug its way bak into the grownd, lukin for food, he suspectid. It was the last that Jad-da thawt befaw the fyre tuk him.

NON-FICTION

NOW THE RIVERS
NO LONGER MEET
THE SEAS

VALENTINE CARTER

The scrawny ginger kitten playing with the end of my shoelace rolled around, joyfully scuffing up enough dust to make it sneeze. The sound of my lighter sparking sent it skittering behind a small tower of Coca-Cola crates stacked outside the bar. I guess it was scared I was going to kick it or scoop it into a carrier bag. It had that look about it. But it was safe with me. I had the kind of hangover that demands you sit still with your back steady against something solid and don't move. The packet was down to two Gauloises. If such a thing is possible, there are two decent legacies from the French colonisation of Tunisia: patisseries everyone likes and cigarettes I like. Smoking French cigarettes makes me feel like the diffident anti-hero who is friends with the Jean-Paul Belmondo character in a Godard movie.

"*Avez-vous une cigarette, pour moi?*" a man said.

I looked at him over the top of my sunglasses and blinked him into focus. He looked like he was made out of long bits of string tied together. He had a very bright grin and curly black hair that needed a wash. I tossed him the packet, which he fumbled.

"*Il ne reste que deux,*" he said, holding them out, handing them back.

"*Ce n'est pas important,*" I said. "*Fumez, fumez. Vas-y.*"

"You're English?" he said.

"I'm from London."

"Is that different?"

"Yeah, very." My head hurt from looking up at his face shadowed against the sunny sky. It was very warm even though it was late December. The north of Tunisia is supposed to have a Mediterranean climate.

"Why are you in Zaghouan? This is a bad time to be in Tunisia," he said, after he'd managed to light his cigarette.

He looked comically serious, in the way that small children do because they've experienced so little that everything seems desperately important. I was going to discount his warning as some kind of anti-tourist shtick, not that I thought of myself as a tourist, then I remembered the unexplained unease on the streets in Tunis that I'd dismissed as lonely-traveller insecurity. The deserted beaches in Hammamet, even quieter than they would be in the off-season. I'd had the Amphitheatre of El Jem almost to myself.

"Why?" I said. *"Pourquoi est-ce mauvais?"* I didn't like speaking English and I could only say love and thank you in Arabic. A good way to get into trouble.

He looked at me as if he was making a decision, then smiled. "Soon Dad will open the bar. Come in" – he pointed at the ginger kitten who was tumbling around my shoes again – "and bring your friend."

It doesn't matter where I travel, I always seem to pick up a stray.

Zaghouan is a small town in the north-east corner of Tunisia. It's full of those familiar small white houses you see on screensavers, with the iconic blue doors and terracotta pots on doorsteps. They line the warm sandy streets, lidded by a cloudless sky. The town is perched on a low ridge on the edge of the Dorsale Mountains and you can see clear across the yellowing fields, pockmarked by squat dark-green trees which in summer start to brown in the unaccustomed heat, as if struck by a new kind of autumn. The Roman Water Temple on the Djebel Zaghouan draws tourists to the town, its ruins forming a crescent of porticos hugging the sacred fountain where water was drawn from a spring and transported via an ancient aqueduct to Carthage, the heart of the Roman Empire in Africa, over 90 km away. The aqueduct could carry between 17 and 32 million litres of water a day. A volume that is almost impossible to imagine when you're standing among the dusty ruins. Times have changed since then. The pace of change continues to accelerate.

"Marhaban, Papa," Marouen greeted the man behind the bar, who had arranged his considerable bulk around a large newspaper spread across the counter.

I coaxed the kitten out of the pocket of my cardigan and carefully draped myself over a chair. Marouen took two beers from the shelf behind the bar and spoke to his father in rapid Arabic. I had to remind myself that it was not argument or aggression I could hear in the cadence and intonation of the words, just my own unfamiliarity echoing back. They were having a long, involved conversation. I could tell that from the gestures they made as I waited for the beer to make its way over to me. I removed my sunglasses and switched them for my regular glasses, then put the kitten on my lap where it wobbled about before it curled up and went to sleep.

The bar was dark after the late-afternoon sun outside and looked like it had once been a schoolroom but, when older, had discovered drink and rock and roll and gone off the rails. More crates were stacked up against the walls and decks of playing cards were lying around. And no customers.

"Is it always this quiet?" I said as Marouen put the bottles on the table and sat down.

"Everyone will be back from work soon," he said. "Or back from looking for work. That's almost a job in itself now."

"What do you do?" I said. The beer was cold. I felt like it was the first cold beer I'd had in Tunisia.

"I am applying for a master's degree," he said. "At the University of Gabès."

"In what?" I said, struck by how I could never tell what class people were in different countries. Or maybe I couldn't tell how it might matter.

"I don't know it in English," he said. "*Valorisation des bio-ressources.*"

I nodded, not sure what *bio-ressources* were, much less *valorisation*.

"It won't happen now though." He plucked at the label on his beer bottle.

"Why not?"

There was no answer. His father coughed, as if shaking out his lungs like a dusty rug, then rustled the pages of his newspaper.

"Because it's a bad time to be in Tunisia?" I said.

His father fired off a sentence or two and I felt uncomfortable that he was listening.

Marouen replied to him and then said to me, "He's annoyed because he can't speak English. And yeah, it's a bad time here."

I didn't say anything. I left a gap in the conversation, the kind of gap that young men often feel compelled to fill with an explanation.

✳

On 17 December 2010, six days before I arrived in Tunisia, Mohamed Bouazizi set himself on fire. Bouazizi was a street vendor in Sidi Bouzid, another historical Roman town in central Tunisia, selling fruit and vegetables. In 2010 Sidi Bouzid was rife with corruption and the unemployment rate was high. In the hours before his self-immolation Bouazizi had gone to see local officials to complain about the police confiscating his produce because he couldn't afford to pay them any more bribes. In response, the officials took his scales. He was so upset by the altercation, which eyewitnesses described as a humiliation, he asked to be referred to the governor's office to escalate the complaint and request his scales back. When the governor refused to see him, he carried out his threat to set himself on fire. He was taken to hospital with severe burns. The torrent of public outrage prompted the then President Zine El Abidine Ben Ali to visit him, promising to send him to a hospital in France. On 4 January 2011, two days after I left, Mohamed Bouazizi died in Tunisia. More than five thousand people joined the funeral procession and one of them was Marouen. He went with his cousins, Ahmed and Fehir.

I didn't know any of this before I met Marouen. Although I can read French much better than I can speak it, well enough to understand at least half of a newspaper, there was no information about Bouazizi anywhere. While Marouen was telling me this story, he sat very still and spoke very quietly. As if he was afraid that the slightest movement or animation might cause an avalanche and he too would come crashing down. Even though we'd only just met I could tell that it meant something particular to him. That the boy who was, at that time, lying in a hospital bed, was more than a street vendor. He was already a symbol, a catalyst. It was in every pause as Marouen tried to find the right word and every nervous shuffle of his father's newspaper. Later I would feel it in the paving slabs and the taxi ranks. It was everywhere.

"The fruit and vegetables he was selling – they were so expensive for him to buy," Marouen said. "He couldn't get any more credit. The situation ..." He trailed off, unable to pluck the rest of the sentence out of the air.

"Why are they so expensive?" I said, thinking of the huge covered market in Tunis with piles of bright-red tomatoes and an extensive range of green leafy vegetables that seemed so abundant. I had wondered at the time who was buying them and who was cooking them, given the consistently terrible food I had been served.

"Farming is hard now," he said. "Not enough rain and then the winds from the mountains are taking the top layer of soil away. This is why I need to study." He banged his fist on the table, frightening my kitten. I placed it on the floor and it dashed away into a corner and disappeared.

"Sorry," Marouen said. "Let's have another drink. I'll get my cigarettes."

When he came back I asked him if his *bio-ressources* were to do with farming.

"I just need to get away from here," he said. "There is nothing for me to do. I don't want to be a barman. And I'm –" He stopped and looked around to see where his father was.

I wanted to tell him that I knew, that he didn't have to say it out loud, but I'd rather he acknowledged it so we could both be clear no one was misunderstanding the situation.

"My boyfriend lives in Gabès," he said so I could only just hear him.

"Isn't that miles away?" I said.

"We write, email."

"That's nice."

"I knew I could tell you," he said. "I thought you were a boy from a distance."

He meant from about two metres. This misconception is not uncommon.

Most of Tunisia, apart from the northernmost third, is a dry desert climate with less than 3.5 cm of rainfall a year. Around three hundred miles south of Tunis is Douz, the gateway to the Sahara, a town of date palms and the strangest hotel I have ever stayed in. It was like the Ancient Egyptian branch of the Overlook Hotel. Eighty per cent of water in Tunisia is used for agriculture. It is unsurprising, then, that climate change, and the loss of what little water they had, has had a huge impact on the industry.

In 2014 the UN held a drought initiative workshop in Cairo to support Tunisia in managing that impact. Two of the bullet points on the final slide from the main presentation were *Emergency Measures* and *Population Migration*. They were actively planning for some areas to become uninhabitable and for emergency scenarios to become a regular occurrence. Perhaps the reason why it's being taken so seriously by the UN is that there is already an example of how wrong things can go if no action is taken.

According to the UN, between 2006 and 2011 the drought in Syria caused 75 per cent of farms to fail and killed 80 per cent of livestock. This catastrophic collapse in farming meant that around 1.5 million Syrians migrated to the cities. A few – dying, desperate and susceptible to propaganda and the promise of a better life – joined the Islamic State of Iraq and the Levant (ISIL), formerly known as the Islamic State of Iraq and Syria. The ensuing civil war has killed almost half a million people. In 2014, at the height of the war, when ISIL declared their caliphate, the de facto capital was Raqqa. Swooping into poverty-stricken areas and scooping up desperate men is an ISIL recruitment strategy. And it works.

Marouen insisted that the bar was busy but by London standards it was deserted. There were a few older men sprawled in chairs as if they were taking root and two younger men in battered leather jackets. Papa had reassured himself that I definitely wasn't French and so had shaken my hand and touched his fingers to his heart afterwards. I always think that's the best handshake in the world. He gifted me a pack of larynx-stripping cigarettes and pressed us to take a bottle of Thibarine back to the table. Thibarine is a date liqueur so sticky and sweet it's almost impossible to remember that it's 40 per cent proof and therefore not to be disrespected. Even the vague smell of dates still makes me feel like the room is listing hard to the left.

"I'm supposed to be on the bus to Hammamet," I said. I had a room booked.

"It's gone," Marouen said.

"Can I get a *louage*?"

"Unlikely," he said. "They'll all be full and you wouldn't be safe anyway. And not to Hammamet. Maybe Tunis."

"Tunis will do."

"Why are you here?" he said.

I told him I'd spent the last three Christmases in North Africa to escape festive jumpers and tinsel and family. I tried not to make myself sound self-indulgent and entitled but I couldn't do much about the fact that I was sitting there with my British passport wandering aimlessly through Marouen's country, curious and interested but still somehow oblivious to everything falling apart around me.

"My family drive me mad, but I love them," he said, nodding.

"My family drive me mad," I said.

There was a change of atmosphere in the bar, like we were in a western and the sheriff had just walked in. Although I couldn't understand what the woman who bustled up to Marouen said, it was obvious she was his mother, even before she took hold of his chin and stared into his face. I heard my name and then in a few short sentences, not all of them translated, it was decided that she, Umi, would feed me. I looked like the stray kitten apparently. I assumed Marouen was paraphrasing.

As we followed Umi towards the house it was as if Marouen had shed about ten years. He suddenly became a gangly adolescent skulking behind her, as if he were in trouble for something his best mate had done. Even I felt more sober in her presence, or at least less drunk. Their home was a long bungalow on the other side of a patchy stretch of grass behind the bar. It looked as if someone had assembled it over a considerable period as building materials, and perhaps regulations, had advanced. We went in the back door, and it was like sliding backwards through time.

The sitting room was similar to the ones I had seen at Matmata, where the dwellings are dug out of the rocks, beautiful curved white walls with seats and tables rising up out of the stone. In Umi's kitchen there were the same white walls, hung with woven blankets, and the simple stove over an open fire. The rest of the house felt like it had been tacked onto these two spaces as the family grew.

Umi fired some rapid words at Marouen.

I looked at him.

"She says to show you the washing machine," he said. "She doesn't want you to think we're backwards."

"I don't think that."

We went into a room that looked like a Western utility room – it was full of things that didn't belong elsewhere. I looked at the washing machine, which still had its cardboard feet on the bottom. Expensive-looking sports kit spilled out of it.

"Where did you get the washing machine from?" I said.

"The governor's office. It washes the team kit. My brother plays volleyball so Umi does their washing."

Marouen glared at the washing machine.

"So he can play?" I asked.

Marouen nodded. "He's good, he should always be in the team, but if Umi doesn't do the laundry he's benched."

"It's just laundry," I said, knowing very well that it wasn't just laundry to Marouen.

We stood in silence contemplating the washing machine.

"Have you eaten a *brik* before?" Marouen said, changing the subject.

I had. In El Jem, on the steep banked seating in the Amphitheatre at half seven in the morning. I lied and said I hadn't as Marouen led me back to the dining room.

Umi put a large plate of golden triangle shapes in the middle of the huge table and, as if hearing some silent signal, five people appeared and sat down with us. It was like being in an American sitcom, surrounded by Marouen's brothers, a cousin and two sisters. A *brik* is a folded pocket of pastry filled with an egg, onion, harissa and sometimes tuna, then deep fried. They can be served with capers and cheese, or olives, but Umi's *briks* didn't need any embellishment. Just the basic *brik*. It was the best meal I had in Tunisia. We ate quickly and conversation flew back and forth across the table. I was introduced to everyone but couldn't hang on to their names and after a while Marouen gave up trying to translate what they were saying. Marouen's older brother seemed a lot older than him and his youngest sister a lot younger. There were three empty chairs at the enormous table and I wondered who was missing. Probably his cousins Ahmed and Fehir. And then as suddenly as they had all appeared, once the meal was over they vanished again.

Marouen yawned. "I'll show you where you can sleep," he said, as if this had all been discussed and agreed.

I looked at my watch. It was only ten.

"Early start tomorrow," he said. "We have to get up at five."

"What for?"

"I'm driving you and some chickens to Tunis."

I must have looked incredulous.

"Seriously. Chickens. Umi's chickens. We need to sell them."

I was expecting an explanation, but he clammed up. I wondered if they were having to pay bribes too. Your son can play volleyball but you have to wash the kit. You can run a bar but you have to pay us half your takings every week, maybe more, we'll see how you go. The dark side of bureaucracy.

"Come on, you can sleep in my little brother's room."

"Where is he?"

"He's in Sidi Bouzid," Marouen said as he guided me out of the room by my elbow. "Don't tell Umi. Papa knows. He said when he comes back he's going to kill him."

The room was small with a tall, thin window looking out on the dark countryside. It seemed very much like a teenager's room and I wondered how old he was and who he'd run away to Sidi Bouzid with. The bed was already made up with clean sheets. I was relieved because on the wall at the end of the bed was a four-foot-high poster of a woman with implausibly large breasts. She wore a Stars and Stripes thong and nothing else. I don't know a lot about teenage boys, or much about revolution, and it was hard to picture the boy who slept in that room on the front line of a social uprising. I guess at that point it still felt to me as though he had a choice, like Marouen had chosen to stay in Zaghouan. But I would come to understand that choice, in Tunisia in 2010, was like the Water Temple. Little more than a monument to something people used to have.

Two days before I arrived in Zaghouan I had been to Carthage. While wandering around the Antonine Baths I'd been stopped from taking a photograph by a huge soldier with a machine gun.

It took me a while to work out what the problem was – there's something about an assault rifle that directs your attention away from anything other than staying alive. I was taking a picture of some columns and in the background, high on a cliff behind the baths, was a modern building: the Tunisian presidential palace, a long white villa with sharp black windows that overlooks Carthage. The then President Ben Ali, it turned out, didn't want people taking photographs of it. It seems that this is a peculiar trait of dictators. In Marrakesh I had the memory card ripped out of my camera and thrown down a drain by a Moroccan soldier because I'd taken a photograph in the vague direction of the palace gates.

This is more than bureaucracy or over-zealous policing. Like much of what happens at the point of a rifle, no matter how trivial the cause might seem, this is a form of oppression. This is the reality of visiting a country with a regime almost celebratory in its disdain for the everyday life of its people.

It was still dark when Marouen met me by his neighbour's truck, the back already loaded with a few crates of chickens. They were noisy and they smelled. They weren't going to help me to nurse my new hangover. The truck didn't want to start but Marouen just laughed and sang the bass line from *Blue Monday* over and over while plucking the steering wheel, claiming it helped. I wondered what day it was. I was in the hinterland between Christmas and New Year, time that's a bit hazy anyway, but even more so on holiday where the days ceased to matter. Unless it was a Monday and the museums were closed. Marouen's neighbour, hearing the complaints of the engine, came out in his pyjamas, reached in through the window and pulled out the choke.

"I could have told you that," I said.

"Wait," the neighbour said. A couple of minutes later he came back with two mugs of thick, black coffee. By the time we left Zaghouan on the pristine grey asphalt road, I was more awake than I had ever been. We listened to a cassette of eighties hits Marouen found in the glove box and watched the bleached landscape emerge as the sun rose and Cyndi Lauper pleaded that *girls just wanna have fuh-un*. We passed the occasional vehicle and a few small towns but mostly everywhere was still and quiet, as if everyone was holding their breath. It was so unnerving that by the time we were on the outskirts of Tunis I'd decided I wanted to go home. I had four days until my flight and not enough money to change it.

When the Tunisian government was overthrown on 14 January 2011 it was described as a bloodless coup. Three people, including Mohamed Bouazizi, lost their lives and more were injured, but compared with what happened in Libya, Yemen and Iraq, some might call it a stately and refined revolution. Tunisia was, and to some extent remains, the great hope of the Arab Spring.

"Go home," Marouen had said as he started the engine again. "Get on a plane soon. You promise me."

I didn't say anything, just nodded and then waved as he drove off. I knew I'd never see or speak to him again.

If the uprising in Tunisia that started the Arab Spring hadn't bracketed my visit, I probably would have forgotten all about him.

On 26 June 2015, thirty-eight people died in Port El Kantaoui, a tourist resort near Sousse, in a terrorist attack. Three months before that, the Bardo Museum in Tunis was attacked by terrorists aligning themselves with ISIL. Twenty-two people died. It's estimated that around three thousand Tunisians are fighting with ISIL, all of them recruited from the poorest areas of the country.

There is a scene in Al Gore's *An Inconvenient Sequel* that takes place in the immediate aftermath of the terror attacks in Paris on 13 November 2015, which included the attacks on the Bataclan and the Stade de France. One hundred and thirty people died. Gore is supposed to be doing a twenty-four-hour event to raise awareness and funding for his climate change work. He stands in front of a majority French audience and tells them how sorry he is. That America stands with them. At no point does he make the link between the events he's trying to prevent and the events unfolding less than a mile away. I suppose it wasn't the time. It never seems to be the time.

*

I spent New Year's Eve alone in a hotel room in Tunis. The ceiling leaked every time the people upstairs had a shower but as it only dripped into the bathroom no one seemed to mind much. Me included. The hotel was on a wide boulevard with trees clustered on narrow strips of grass in the centre. A main thoroughfare with four lanes of traffic that in many capital cities of the world would have been an exemplar of giddy New Year's Eve chaos.

Since leaving Marouen I'd wandered about Tunis, mooched around a few museums and made my customary visit to a random cemetery. The city felt on edge. I felt unsafe. Alone. I couldn't work out whether the number of police and soldiers on the streets was normal or a new precaution. It felt oppressive. As if we were waiting for something. Groups of young men would come together on street corners or outside cafés and then disperse almost as soon as they had arrived. They had clearly done something, achieved what they'd come for, but I couldn't figure out what it was. I became an expert at glancing, only allowing my gaze to flit around. I was terrified of being accused of staring. It wasn't only the spoken language I didn't understand but the body language, the way the street spoke. There was nothing in the news pages or on the television. I watched BBC News 24 and no one mentioned Tunisia. The Foreign Office had no advice. The British embassy looked impenetrable and unconcerned, as British embassies tend to do. I took to hanging out in a French bookshop because it was the most European place, the most certain place I could find. The owner smoked American Spirit cigarettes. I remember the smell of the smoke on the spines of the books and how well it suited a Dorothy Parker collection they had. My Jean-Paul Belmondo fantasies seemed pathetic. I read *L'Équipe* daily as a futile attempt at distraction. There wasn't a stray cat or dog to be found anywhere.

At quarter past midnight on New Year's Eve a white sports car, maybe a Lamborghini, roared down the road with three people hanging out of its windows screaming with laughter and waving bottles and flags. From my hotel balcony I watched them disappear between the trees. As I leaned over, with a cigarette and a glass of something pretending to be champagne, high above everything, I reminded myself that my flight was at dawn in two days and I could escape. I appreciated how lucky I was then, and now I'm grateful that I didn't get to see what was coming. You don't watch a coup from the sidelines, no matter how bloodless it might be.

I know it's not just drought or high unemployment that turns people into fighters or murderers. It's more complicated than that. But you can't ignore the impact they have. If you take away people's livelihoods and their homes and put them under extraordinary pressure then those people will react. And as global temperatures rise it will get harder and harder for some communities to survive. Many of those communities are already struggling with poverty and they are struggling alone.

The disdain for the everyday lives of the people that dictators display is the same disdain that drives our politicians, not just the leaders of Maghreb or Middle Eastern countries. This is the disdain that ultimately tells former chancellors, senators, presidents and policy makers in the US, the UK and Europe that it doesn't matter if temperatures rise, farms fail and livestock die. It doesn't matter, they say to each other in Davos, because we can still fill those covered markets that wealthy people walk their chihuahuas through, we can still fill them with all the bright fruits and vegetables needed to promote our image. Never mind what we feed the people who can't afford to buy them. The people who can't farm or work any more because there's no water, only a wind full of heat and dust.

When the little time we have left runs out, and everyone's everyday lives ebb away, it won't be the tonnes of water flooding our cities, or catastrophic heatwaves, or the freezing snowfall that will kill us. It will be war in all its many forms. Whether the formal strategic kind waged by governments, like those in Syria or Yemen, or the terror attacks on bridges or at pop concerts, like those where we live. Where we get to fly home to.

FICTION

BOOM BABIES

ANDREW LEACH

I f the camera panned around slowly we would see a minimalist office, or maybe an open-plan kitchen with plate-glass sliding windows and a view of the ocean. On a polished island counter with a sparkling stone surface there would be a high-tech laptop next to a juicer and a sculpted fruit bowl cradling peaches, kiwis, apples. The camera would glide over the fruit suggesting a wholesome, healthy lifestyle and would come to rest on the computer. It would linger on the screen, on which we see an emerging pattern of red dots.

The movie soundtrack would be a specific song playing softly in the background. It's a cover version, something edgy – perhaps Talking Heads' *Burning Down the House*, for reasons that will become clear in a moment – but on an acoustic guitar or a piano.

You would realise that what we're looking at on the computer is a map and Margot Robbie would lean in close to the screen and say "Oh my God" and the dots would glow red like cherries, or like those little stickers that get put on a wall in an art gallery next to a picture that's been sold. And if that's what it made you think of you might go "Wow, that's one heck of a gallery."

Margot would say "Hey, come and look at this," and Ryan Gosling would step into shot and lean in *closer* to the laptop and Margot would say something like "The world is burning."

Wildfires.

Each red dot represents a wildfire.

The landscape a whole ossuary of dry.

The world is burning.

California, Texas, the mountains of southern Europe, Greece and Spain and Italy. South Africa, Australia. The moors above Manchester. Sweden. Siberia. The Arctic Circle.

Think about those last few for a minute.

Ryan would say something like "How can this happen?" because despite being smart enough to hold down a job as a lawyer and earning enough money to afford a beachfront property and, as we'll later discover, an apartment in the city, he recognises the need for dialogue that helps us move the plot along even if it sounds like he really ought to get it straight off the bat.

"Humans are literally setting fire to the planet," Margot says.

In a first draft of the script Ryan might have said "What, you mean arson?" but he's not that dumb because lawyer, et cetera, and now he stays quiet as Margot says that every one of these dots represents a discarded cigarette, a small-time barbecue, a piece of glass from a broken bottle reflecting the sun, kids building campfires, and yes, some of them are started deliberately by people who look suspiciously like Javier Bardem.

And the camera will sweep away, out of the kitchen, out of the house, along the beach and into the dunes, panning out, widening the view, travelling miles by helicopter until we're over a great fire and people are running and sirens are squawking and smoke is blanketing treetops before blooming into the sky like ink swirling in water and flames are crackling and hauling themselves higher into the forest and ash is dancing like a black snowstorm and the music is no longer the cover version but has become the original recording and the volume is cranked and it goes ba-ba-ba, ba-da-ba-ba-da.

Except
this isn't
a movie.

* * * * *

I wake with the little red dots still burning holes behind my eyes. Turn off the quiet burble of my phone's alarm. I reach out for Lachlan but instead my sleepy hand touches Brett's shoulder.

He murmurs "You OK honey?" and I tell him "Yes" and say "Go back to sleep."

I lean over and lightly kiss his temple and he makes a low sighing, bovine noise.

The clock on Brett's side of the bed says 05:15 and I slip from beneath the sheet and put on my robe, creep out of the bedroom in the hope that he'll sleep on.

In the kitchen I make tea and think about phoning Lachlan but the clock on the oven says 05:21 and I don't think he'd thank me.

My laptop sits closed on the counter and I'm grateful for the links Cassie sent over last night. The drama contained in graphics that render the whole world ablaze, the little red spots spreading out like a virus, and the truth bomb that I'm planning on detonating later today.

Outside the sun's already been up for half an hour and yesterday's heat still hangs in the air, waiting to be topped up like a Caribbean tan. Like a bed that still holds the warmth of the last person to lie in it as you climb in between sheets that need changing and I think about Lachlan, his head on the pillow, and I silently chide myself for holding the image somewhere on my brain's hard drive.

The small urban garden visible through the kitchen window looks like it's been bleached, green seared to yellow-white, brown earth to beige dust.

A car's coming for me at quarter to. I take my tea into the bathroom.

The car's a Prius, which is at least something.

I'm wondering why I've agreed to take part in this.

An early-morning duel live on the radio about the need for more renewable energy sources following the release of a report from a so-called think-tank claiming there's no appetite for solar and wind power.

The adversary the BBC has decided to pitch me against is my uncle.

I'd asked a couple of people in my organisation whether they thought I should do it and once it had been established that there's no love lost between dear old Uncle David and me, they seemed to think it would get good coverage and help reinforce our argument. Someone who thought he was clever said "It's *Kramer vs. Kramer* all over again," and I said "It's not spelled the same, we're Cramer with a C," and he said "But still."

A child at the BBC, who had at least been trying to do some homework, called me to arrange the interview. They asked if I'd prefer to use my married name and I'd said "What do you mean, 'married name'?" being deliberately obtuse.

They said "Isn't your husband Brett Loeb?" and I said "Yes, but that's his name, not mine."

It only took for them to say "But –" for me to say "He married me, he didn't brand me."

I remember breathing deeply and feeling regretful about being so spiky.

"I'm sorry," I said. "But my name is Astrid Cramer. If you'd like to embellish it further, my middle name is Violet, after my grandmother, and I have a master's in environmental planning so you can use MSc too, if you like. I didn't take my husband's name and don't intend to. Just as he didn't take mine."

They apologised and said they didn't mean any offence, but I cut them off and said it was OK and no offence taken. If I were them I would have just hung up.

So now I'm sitting in the back of the Toyota Prius that's already getting snarled in city traffic, which for the most part is still spewing particulates into the not-so-sweet morning air, on my way to a BBC studio where my uncle will be presented as somehow providing balance to a decades-old debate about whether climate change is an actual thing and how much longer we can continue to relegate wind and solar energy to bit parts, when in reality the debate should be about how we're going to make wind and solar the go-to option and the whole thing is, frankly, a fucking sham.

Outside the car window a poster advertising a breakfast cereal says GET READY FOR A BRAND NEW WORLD and a yellow cartoon sun grins like a celestial emoji over a field of golden corn and I think You don't know the half of it, sunshine.

∗ ∗ ∗ ∗ ∗

The camera climbs into the back seat and we see Margot-slash-Astrid put on a pair of aviator sunglasses. She turns towards the camera and tilts her blond head downwards, looks at us over the rims. She sighs.

"Uncle David," she says. "He's –"

She pauses, seeking the right word.

She removes the sunglasses completely and stares straight down the lens.

"– well, a bit of a wanker, really."

Another sigh, this one more exasperation than resignation.

She puts the sunglasses back on. Then:

"He's my father's older brother. Worked in oil, became an MP in '92 and was then a part of Tony Blair's government in '97. Made a junior minister in the old Ministry of Food and when that became the Department for Environment, Food and Rural Affairs he managed to get himself promoted. So now we have someone from the oil industry in charge of the environment, which is a recipe for a clusterfuck.

"He lost his seat in 2010. Went back into oil, now heads the think-tank on energy policy which has released the report and advises all sorts of climate change deniers, protecting vested interests in business. So, as I said, he's a bit of a wanker. Oh, and his daughter-in-law – not that he acknowledges her as such – is Cassie. She's my mentor, and the one who sent me the links."

Margot-slash-Astrid settles back in the seat, takes a piece of paper from her satchel and starts to read.

The camera pulls away and cuts to a shot of her car effortlessly cruising through London's streets, the traffic having miraculously diminished, before pulling up outside a large glass-fronted building. The camera sweeps across a sign that says *BBC*.

✳ ✳ ✳ ✳ ✳

I'm in the studio with a pair of oversized headphones clamped to my ears listening to Nicholas, the presenter, say "And with me to discuss it is a former minister for the environment under Tony Blair, David Cramer, who now chairs the think-tank the Centre for Energy Reform, and the environmental campaigner and writer Astrid Cramer, who also happens to be David's niece," and he says it like it's a major deal, his voice rising in pitch at the end of the sentence like he's just found out.

Nicholas says "David, let me start with you," and he sets out the report's conclusions, which pretty much amount to building more wind and solar facilities being uneconomic and that nuclear and what it calls "clean coal" are the ways forward, essentially ignoring thirty years of progress.

And then I'm watching David's thin, lizard lips move and it's a wonder we're related and I'm thankful that I look more like my mother than my father's side of the family, his voice droning into my head like a wasp from somewhere inside the headphones.

I hear the presenter say "Astrid Cramer, what do you make of that?" and I shuffle in my seat and sit up straight.

"Well," I say, "as David knows I was brought up to be polite but frankly I've never heard such a load of old agenda-driven rubbish, even by his standards."

Presenter Nicholas chortles and makes the word "OK" last longer than it should.

David's face suddenly reminds me of my father's the first time he found cigarettes in my room when I was about fourteen.

"I think what's really relevant today," I say, "is to establish who funds the Centre for Energy Reform."

Nicholas, clearly expecting me to rebut David's statements and insist that everyone engage with renewable energy, simply says "David?"

"I don't see what that's got to do with anything," David says.

"Then let me tell you," I say, all smiles and sweet little niece. "You've just explained to the listeners that your organisation recommends the country stop exploring renewable energy sources."

David says "Yes."

"You want the UK to reinvest in big traditional industries, despite the fact that the break-even point for solar, wind and other types of renewables is getting lower all the time."

David says "Yes, but –"

I say "Please, David, if I can finish."

Nicholas says "You've had your turn, David. Let's hear what Astrid has to say."

David glares.

I say "In many countries, renewables are now the most economic form of energy. And, of course, investing in offshore energy sources could hugely rejuvenate areas such as south Wales and the north-east of England."

David tries to intervene, saying "It's really not that simple but I do think some of the more forward-looking traditional sources can be better value, yes."

I ignore his interjection.

"And yet what you haven't told people is that those traditional industries are the ones funding your research," I say.

"That's simply not true," David says.

"Really? I think I can prove differently."

* * * * *

The camera's suspended high up in the studio, like CCTV. It's showing us what happens next as an instrumental version of *Burning Down the House* plays, allowing itself to become a different metaphor. The scene may be in black and white, something the director will decide at a later date in the editing suite.

We see David Cramer stand and yank off his headphones, throw them onto the desk. We see him shouting silently as the music plays, first at the presenter and then at Margot-slash-Astrid who is still sitting, and he's jabbing his finger and we read his lips as he calls her a "little fucking bitch".

She remains calm and says something to him and his assistant enters the studio and tries to manoeuvre David from the room, and he's still shouting and the presenter is trying to reason with him and the director calls "CUT –"

* * * * *

I'm at lunch in a pizza-chain restaurant with Hilary.

After I left the radio studio I went into the office but I couldn't get anything done as my phone kept either ringing or sending through alert after alert, so I took myself out for a walk to clear my head. My Twitter notifications have been going crazy and I keep reading that I *owned* David Cramer, an expression I've always found a little obnoxious. I am, apparently, *trending*.

Among the list of missed calls is one from Lachlan and two more from my father. I have several unopened voicemails.

The only calls I've taken have been from Brett and Cassie.

Brett said he was proud of me and that I sounded calm and in control, which wasn't how I'd felt inside but was at least the impression I wanted to create. When he rang off he said "Love you" and I said "Love you too," although after a year of marriage I'm already aware that we use the words as punctuation, like "How are you?" or "See you later."

Cassie called from San Francisco to say she'd listened via the Internet and that she, too, was proud. Her husband, Stuart, David's son, was out for the evening and hadn't heard it yet. Cassie was pretty sure that he would piss himself.

Hilary pushes her salad around with her fork and says "So how was the radio thing?" before lifting some dressed green leaves towards her beautiful teeth. I watch as her mouth closes over them, momentarily transfixed by the smoothness of her dark skin.

"I take it you didn't hear it," I say.

Hilary says "Uh-uh."

She swallows and says "Sorry, babe. Completely forgot. Besides, me and Radio 4 aren't really acquainted, you know?" and she pulls a face.

For some reason this pleases me immensely.

"It went well," I say, picking up a piece of pizza crust. "I pretty much called my uncle a liar live on air."

Hilary grins and says "You're off his Christmas card list, then."

"Something like that," I say.

I don't want to talk about it any more and I say "So how's Marlon?"

"He's fine," she says. "Things are good. Looks like he might be sent to the States for three months on secondment, which is exciting."

"Cool," I say. "Whereabouts?"

"LA."

"Nice. You going too?"

"Hoping to," she says. "Trying to organise a little sabbatical at work."

She laughs like she's sharing a private joke with herself. Takes a sip of Sauvignon Blanc from her glass.

I smile too, say "What is it?"

"Marlon," she says. "He's ... well, he said we should go to Vegas while we're out there. Maybe, you know, tie the knot, Vegas-style."

"That's great," I say, meaning it. "Does that mean congratulations are in order?"

We're both laughing now as she says "Ah, I don't know yet. Let's just see what happens. But we're talking about it. And don't you say a word."

"I won't," I say. "Promise. Our little secret."

I put the last piece of Fiorentina pizza into my mouth and pour myself some more San Pellegrino water.

"Talking of secrets," Hilary says. "When I saw you last month, at that art thing."

"Mm," I say, chewing on the pizza.

"That guy you were with," she says. "That guy who wasn't Brett."

For a split second I get a rush, like I've stepped off the planet and am floating in my own universe and this could either be the best thing ever or could bring worlds crashing down and I don't care which.

I swallow and say "That was Lachlan, my cousin."

Hilary says "Your cousin?" Her eyes wide.

"Yes. My cousin."

"Girl, no way was that your cousin," she says.

I laugh, say "Honestly, it was. My cousin Lachlan."

"Way you were looking at each other?"

"What do you mean?"

"Astrid, babe," she says. "How long have I known you?"

"A while," I say. "Five, six years."

Hilary raises an eyebrow and says simply "Your cousin."

"Yep."

"And there's nothing you want to tell me?"

I reach across the table and squeeze her hand.

"Hils," I say. "I was there with my cousin Lachlan. We're very close. We hang out together a lot, especially when Brett's away. But there's nothing more to say, honest."

She shrugs and says "OK," and we're back to talking about her and Marlon's impending trip to the States and I feel an empty pang of something I decide is envy since I miss being on the west coast of America and I can't wait to go back and I ignore the tiny voice that tells me the feeling might be something else.

It's sometime after ten. I only got in half an hour ago. It feels like I've been up for days.

I hear Lachlan say "I just want to see you again, you know?"

His voice in my ear tries to drag me back to a place when we were younger but I'm tired and I say "Lackie, things have moved on now."

The room's lit by a solitary table lamp that throws long shadows up the pale-grey wall and across the Georgia O'Keeffe print. I've got music playing softly in the background but I'm not sure what it is. Something I started streaming and then forgot about when my phone made its dying-hornet buzz. I was thinking of going to bed but wanted to wait up for Brett. The window's open to let in what breeze there is. Occasional traffic noises climb the outside walls and sneak in like ghosts rushing to somewhere else.

"So what are you saying?" Lachlan asks.

"I'm saying I'm tired. It's been a very long day." And then I relent and say "I want to see you too, but I'm not sure when. Work's busy, we're just starting on a new campaign and I need to finish my book, and Brett's got a lot on too. We might be going to the States soon, I'm not sure. I can't just drop everything like before."

Lachlan says "I know, I don't expect you to. I just miss you."

"You saw me last month," I say. "Less than a month, three weeks ago."

He says "I know." And then he says "Do you remember that drawing I did in Mallorca, when we were kids? The one of your dad's house, but I changed it and made it into an eco-house."

I say "Of course."

And I think "Kids" is pushing it, I was eighteen. But there are a lot of things about that long weekend that I'll never forget. Not least what happened between Lachlan and me. Despite everything the memory sends a thrill coursing through me.

"The building I'm working on now," he says. "The one in Wales, for that actor I told you about."

"Uh-huh."

"I realised today," he says. "It's just like a version of the house I drew then." And then he adds "I guess that's why I'm so keen to see you now. I've been thinking about you all day."

"You're sweet," I say. "It's nice to know that someone's thinking about me."

There's a pause and it's like we're both just floating in that pool in Mallorca, fingertips occasionally touching but letting the amniotic water do all the work and it's safe and wild and secret. The sunshine throwing silver shards into the blue.

"I'll see you soon," I say, "I promise. Look after yourself, lovely Lackie," and I hang up.

I sit for a while sipping a glass of soda and lime. The ice has long since melted and it feels like a reminder that tomorrow's going to be another long day working on a campaign that focuses on a world underwater by 2070 due to the melting polar ice caps. I'm briefing an artist who's going to be producing a piece of animation that we're hoping to enter for film festivals and my mind connects "artist" with the art show that Hilary talked about at which all the work seemed so passive and derivative. It was where I last saw Lachlan and we were anything but passive, kissing in that stairwell and giving in again to the impulse that's existed since forever and his mouth's on mine and his hand's inside my dress and I hear Brett's key in the lock.

I wake in darkness. My mind's whirring about something and I know I'm not going to get back to sleep. I get up and take my robe from the hook on the back of the bedroom door. The clock glows 04:28.

I walk into the room Brett and I both use as a study. I open the slatted blind a little and a staircase of moonlight tumbles in and splashes the walls. I stand at the window peering out at the hazy pearl of a moon. Within twenty minutes or so its nemesis will be rising to take centre stage and push it into the background again. I stand staring out, thinking through the notion that had almost shaken me awake, ordering my thoughts.

I open my laptop and put on my headphones. Plug my phone into the MacBook. I download something I recorded yesterday and start to listen to bursts of it. I look at a picture on my phone of a storyboard, a rough draft of a panel of animation the artist produced for me. Slowly, inexpertly, I begin to edit the recording, pausing and grabbing little pieces of it. Brightening the sound so it's not as muffled.

Brett comes into the room, makes me jump by putting his hands on my shoulders. He's naked and he brings with him a soft scent of a half-asleep hot July dawn.

I pull off my headphones and hear him laugh, that quiet San Francisco Bay chuckle he has.

"You frightened the life out of me."

"Sorry, honey."

He bends down and kisses the top of my head.

"What're you up to?"

"You know that animation I told you about?"

"Yeah, sounded pretty cool."

"I'm just playing with some audio for it," I say. "Just one little segment. I woke up thinking about it."

I turn up the volume on the laptop so that Brett can hear.

"I'm thinking of this over some dramatic images of hurricanes," I say.

Wind power. It's just a loony-left conspiracy. Loony-left. L-l-l-loony-left –

Brett laughs.

"Is that your uncle?" he asks.

"Sure is," I say. "Now imagine a shot of a tsunami breaking over a village."

The power of the waves. It's just a loony-left conspiracy. Loony-left. L-l-l-loony-left –

"You recorded the whole interview?" he says.

"Yeah. And what came after it."

"What did come after it?"

I slide the cursor along a line of sound, press Play.

Little fucking bitch.

I press it again.

Little fucking bitch.

Brett says "Is that still David?"

"Uh-huh."

"Oh, that's good. You've got David Cramer on tape calling you a little fucking bitch in response to being called out."

I laugh and say "I seem to, don't I? I wonder how that happened?"

Brett sniggers, says "You're bad. That sort of thing can come in useful."

"That was my thinking too," I say.

"But he knows that you're my little fucking bitch?"

I smile and say "I guess he doesn't."

He takes my hand and pulls me out of the chair.

He leads me back to bed and we fall on top of hot, crumpled sheets and make love.

Afterwards we lay sprawled across each other like two victims, a small abandoned heap of naked limbs and body parts entwined on a cotton killing field. The day unfolding.

Brett drifts back into sleep and I lie there staring at the white ceiling, feeling an incoming tide of heat wash over us and gently set fire to the edges. I untangle myself from Brett and walk naked to the bathroom where I stand and look at myself in the mirror watching the flush on my skin soften, a fading wildfire.

FICTION

THE SHORT CUT

CARMEL SHORTALL

Roisín skipped along the path into town, aware that she was scuffing her good shoes. She was careful not to stand on the cracks of the pavement though. Step on three and the devil you'll see!

Above her, Protestant flags capered and strutted in the breeze like marchers on the Twelfth of July. She counted the flags and gave them their names: Union Jack; Red Hand of Ulster; Vanguard; Union Jack again. The chilly morning air was warming now and Roisín pulled off the itchy cardigan she had been forced to wear.

"They have their oul' flegs up for the Twelfth already," she had heard her granny complain that morning. She only started listening when Mam shushed Granny by saying that little wans have big ears. They meant her. They had stopped talking and it was then that they bundled her into the cardigan and out the door. Now she tied it around her waist, giving it a good stretch in the arms. She skipped on down the road.

As it was Saturday, her friend Maggie would be waiting at her granny's house in Tin Town. She hoped the old doll would be wearing her false teeth so she could understand a word she said. Maggie's da would be sleeping off a hangover so their house was off-limits – unless you wanted to tiptoe about the place. If it had been a weekday, he would have been at work and they could have raced through the house and down to the plum orchard. She loved playing hide-and-seek among the trees this early in the summer – before it filled up with wasps, tipsy and spoiling for a fight from gorging on the fast-fermenting plums.

There'd be no flags hanging out of the prefabs in Tin Town, annoying people and making them cross, she thought as she left the Protestant houses behind. She decided to take the short cut and left the path to cross the rough field where the circus, then the funfair, would pitch their tents every year. They hadn't come last year and wouldn't come this one either – because of The Troubles, Mam said. Bloomin' Troubles!

Roisín missed the funfair. Missed standing on the seats of the swing boats, pulling hard on the rope with Maggie to see how high they could fly; her wee sister Ann-Marie crouched between their legs, screeching with fear and delight. She missed the Rickety Wheel with its tickets and prizes of bags of golden fish, and she missed riding round and round in whirling circles on hobby horses painted the colours of fairy tales.

Roisín reached the trees on the far side of the field. She closed her eyes and let the green light dance on her eyelids as, above her head, sharp-toothed leaves drifted in and out of the sunlight. She held up her arms to the sun's warmth before squeezing herself through the bushes into the shade where the damp earth was musty and slippery. She crept carefully along the back wall of the old storeroom to avoid sliding into the little stream that trickled along beneath it.

"Don't touch the water – you'll get polio!" she heard Maggie say as if she were there. Maggie saw menace everywhere. If you touched the pinky whiteness of hawthorn blossom you'd die of poison or if you picked up a ring glinting innocently on the road, the ground beneath your feet would open up and swallow you down to Hell.

Roisín knew it was all mad dog shite – except maybe the bit about the polio – but why would you risk it – even though Mam had told her that she'd had an injection for polio when she was little and peed herself, putting a big stain on Mam's skirt.

She crept along to where the stream opened out into a small sheltered area, hidden from the outside world by the mossy wall of the storeroom, the guardian trees whose leaves and dancing catkins were never still, and a thick hedge, like the one around Sleeping Beauty's castle, behind Main Street. Once, she thought she heard the thundering of hooves and waited, perfectly still, for a fairy-tale horse to burst through the trees, but it was only an armoured car trundling down the street. Roisín took this short cut into town unless it was raining and the field was flooded. In here, it could be damp but never truly muddy and she often dallied, poking sticks into the stream, looking for invisible fish, so that it wasn't really a short cut but a delay to her journey.

Today there were bottles choking the stream. Bad boys had been here – invaders in her secret place. She heard voices on the other side of the hedge and froze. Maybe they were coming back to drink more bottles of stout. But then she heard the crackling of walkie-talkies, the clatter of running feet and the funny sharp voices of British soldiers. They moved on quickly and she could breathe again.

Roisín promised herself she would come here every day in the summer. She picked up a stick and turned a stone over with it. A millipede and some woodlice crawled about in panic.

An army helicopter buzzed into the edges of her hearing and made its way across the sky till it was overhead, shattering the quiet. It really was very quiet for a Saturday. She looked up as it hovered over her and she imagined all the little Brits in it looking down. Then the 'copter tilted and yammered away into the distance again.

It was time to meet Maggie. All Roisín had to do was walk down the long dry side of the store and across the yard before crawling under the bushy hedge and she would be on Main Street. When she emerged from the bushes, covered in grit, it took her a few seconds to realise that something was not right.

The street was empty. Not a soul about. And the shops … The doors were open and no one was inside. Roisín ran up to Costelloe's and stood on the step looking in at the jars of sweets, shining like jewels, the bars of chocolate, the bags of her favourite cheese and onion crisps … Backing away from temptation, she found herself in the street again and walked a few more paces towards the top of the town.

The helicopter reached its lowest ebb then grew louder as it came close again. Now Roisín noticed the street wasn't empty – a car sat a few yards away. There was something wrong about that but she couldn't think what. She walked up to it slowly and looked in the window. No one was inside. Mam always made her wait in the car now, instead of taking her into the shops. An empty car was an unattended vehicle! A car should have someone in it in a Control Zone so everybody would know it wasn't a bomb.

Roisín stood frozen beside the car. Her heart hammered as dust began to swirl around her feet under the roaring of the helicopter. Squinting downwind, she could just make out a dark cloud of movement at the top of the street in the direction of Tin Town and, as she looked, it seemed that one piece of the cloud detached itself and ran – ever so slowly – towards her. It grew and then it started to shout at her in harsh, foreign tones. "Oi, wot you doin' there? Where the fack d'you come from?"

The Brit reached her and grabbed at her, lifting her by the arm. He shouted again as, speechless now, she pointed with her other arm to the bushes she had crawled under just moments before. The helicopter thundered overhead, louder and closer now and adding to her confusion. An RUC policeman dashed up behind the soldier and tried to drag the pair of them off shouting, "C'mon, c'mon, she's only a we'an." They both ran, dragging Roisín between them.

The moving cloud at the top of the street came into focus and she saw that it was only the people of the town, held back by the police and army. They murmured at her in wonder – where had she come from? The RUC man let her go but the soldier's questions started again. How had she got into the town when the streets were cordoned off? Didn't she know there was a bomb scare? He shook her arm. She felt her face crumple and fought the tears.

"The short cut," she stammered, but she was still thinking about the empty car. The RUC man backed her up.

"There's a short cut from the circus field – the we'ans use it," he said. "They're small enough to juke under the bushes."

A burning cigarette butt came sailing out from the crowd to land nearby and someone shouted out, "Leave her alone, ya fuckin' Brit!"

The townspeople shifted, many feet moving a few steps in one direction, then back again. The soldier looked at the crowd, then Roisín, before saying to the RUC man, "Well tha'll change." He dropped her arm and clumped away.

Roisín tried to get through the crowd but couldn't. A woman in a headscarf patted her shoulder and tried to keep her still. Suddenly, a hand grabbed her by the hair, giving it a good tug. She heard Maggie's muffled voice.

"C'mere you eejit!"

Maggie dragged Roisín through the crowd and away from the attention of the men in uniform.

"You should have seen the cut of you flyin' up that street between them two boys. Thought you were arrested and goin' to jail for sure. You have to sleep on a wooden bed in jail. And you only get one blanket!"

Maggie bobbed up and down, looking for more excitement, but there was none. Within half an hour the all-clear was given and people were allowed to return to their shops and their shopping. No bomb – only a bomb scare.

Maggie's granny had her teeth in and made them a fry of eggs and potato bread followed by tea and pink wafer biscuits. Later, they walked back into town to buy sweets. Roisín noticed that there was no empty car on the road this time but several soldiers and RUC men were examining the short cut – poking around in the bushes, behind the bushes, and along the wall of the old storeroom, tramping into the stream, heedless of the dangers of polio or hawthorn.

When Roisín got home that evening she was in trouble with Mam for traipsing about the town in a bomb scare, trying to get herself killed. As if she could have known. She tried to point this out, but it was no use. Mam shouted and cried. Her granny tried to soothe things by saying there wouldn't be a word about it in a hundred years. That didn't do any good either. She was forbidden to use the short cut again and she wasn't allowed out on her own for days.

And they were hot, sunny days when she could have been running through the orchard with Maggie, or looking for fish in the short cut's secret stream. On the third day Maggie was allowed to visit and the two of them played in the back garden, foraging for peas and chewing on sour leaves of cuckoo sorrel until Maggie pointed out that the leaves were probably full of squirming parasites like you would see down a microscope. After that they trawled the road in front of the house with sticks, looking for tar bubbles to pop, then sat on the kerb complaining about the unfairness of mams and dads.

In the evenings, instead of playing outside until the light died, they gathered around the television in the corner of the kitchen to watch the flickering black-and-white images. Loyalists attacking students marching for civil rights; RUC men raining baton blows on marchers' bodies. The blood was black, unreal, on the television. A man with a thick head of curls dabbed at the dark clot creeping down his forehead, the colour of his hair.

The following Saturday, Roisín was allowed out by herself again and she hurried over the field to the short cut to make sure the stream hadn't dried up in the heat. But the entrance was barred with breeze blocks and when she took the long way round to Main Street, to where the low bushes were, she found that they were all tangled up with barbed wire. She headed on up the busy street towards Tin Town, scuffing her shoes as she went.

POETRY

(NOT WRITING A POEM ABOUT)
  THE "RENEWED HOSTILITIES"

FRAN LOCK

and where were you? in the long outpouring and the pouring
out. mouths gone gangrenous from tact, you were waiting. said
isn't it a roaring shame? our youth consumed by what our youth
consumes. shape of a young boy blown, sworn in chalk, broken
up over a slack blue flame. shit. it isn't love comes in at the eye.
wet paint we licked from terrace ends. to *keen* is not to cry. i
swept my friends from mantelpieces. where were you? the smell
of rain on rust. his face in grief's prescription mirrors, angled
at the sky. i will return. will ride past restive acres of meat. for
him. again. as always. make an ill wind of our weeping. lyre,
liar. lyra. lamentations, prophecies. *too young to remember the
worst of the terror*, invented our own. mise éire. ecstatic and
condemned by turns. *write a poem*, someone said. >> now more
than anything else i fear being asked what i think. old bitches in
inflexible couture with lipstick on their teeth going *what do you
think?* i think that thought is a form of autopsy. i wanted to be
joan of arc, a toothless tomboy belching doves. i think i cried
for him so long his name became a pious cough, the stifled fright
we hide behind our hands, a mean clear taste like vodka over ice
and lime. teenagers always end in tears. goose-fleshed truant skin
made hole. consent. conquest. a red, pent rage they cut us from,
they cut from us. to feel its pinch, its rubberised meniscus suck,
its peel and sweat, its bright and vicious clinging. where were
you? dressing dark, in stains, in skins of smug endangerment.
to step into *our* streets. somewhere between a *dare*, a *risk*. and
dawn is not a chorus but an orgy here. love, love is a dirge you
can drink. percentages and proofs. indictments, degradations,
flesh. girl bodies. bulimic swooning bait. are threaded, stuffed,
and hooked. you stood before our murals. stood in front of
battlements and flags. you crossed our tundra, turned our earth.
our words, our deeds. took photos and struck poses. stuck. in
shiny necrophile fragments. you. instagrammed yourself appalled.
you, who live, not in your landscapes, but your networks, cannot
ever understand. your white incisors incline towards meat. *poet.*
anywhere the blood is scented, trending, squared. girls in skinny

amphetamine pique. are tea-cup breeds with brittle bones. our frail infection vectors. boys with thin, deceptive wounds like fruit machines. these wounds you feed and fuck - - - off back. behind demilitarised pentameters. what i think is *where were you?* thought's an antiseptic fraud. our boys our girls. most penetrable celts. disrupt. undo. these *waifs and strays.* our succulents and phantoms. shit. our sympathetic wounded. *twist of winter,* turn of stair, i heard them howl. *christ died because he could.* these breathing remedial ghosts. i saw them there. i see them now. how night rolls over everything, its lethal fleece. dousing, dosed, and ducking under arcs of orange fire. all children here. our fear a gutless pheromone. our pigeon-chested pedigree. out on sullen escapades. we breathe the spores of sexless dread the same. it keeps us young. it makes us hard. and every tear, a bad tattoo. but who are *you?* sparkling in a cruel financial light, measuring the world into prissy edible segments. >> befoul my palm with silver, i will tell you *all about* our lives. home as a *perverse inversion of light.* a blood fact treading endless water. *death* as symbol. *death* as structure. ugly world of pacts and cults, ingenious offences. sent to the sanitised angst of wards. was seismic and beset. was set. like fruit in dessert gelatine, pale woman in a window. always how his mouth was moth to mine. committing his shivering enterprise. and when he died his empty trainers were the origin of longing. in homes they scrimped on everything but salt. we walked the ramparts in a trance, and vengeance was the ache of idle hands, and day by day. in trackies and in gangs. the doleful blushing tedium of church. a priest adept at finding fault. mothers on the melancholy treadmill of their pregnancy. a rush of blood, a brother for the ranks, and christ, his heart of rich, defeatist praline. where were you? his body a kind of musical wound. and boys, baroque apostles, gaunt-seraphic under earth, on building sites, in ditches. you were not there. his father beat his fists to bloody rusks against the brick. everything. emboldened by, emblazoned with. his mother tore her hair, went barking sweeney, chewing grass. and i - - - i fought the sea in a tiered dress and train for the longest time. where's *your* rage? where's your black flag and valiant heart? >> poet. lack of sleep had made me fearless, so i told you to *fuck off.*

*

for the months i lived on green glass marbles, on frenzy and telepathy. deficiency. enchantment. everything both doubled and divided. >> what a world! << to lie awake and hear your cells, tending towards entropy. and i became a doll. and i became a victorian locket, its brass mouth stuffed with virgin's hair. and what are you *woke* from, or to? on my walk to work i count things into omen: dogs, bottles, women sleeping rough. shouldn't be *reaction* but *refusal*, protest. all-encompassing and severe. i do not want god's grace i want his fury. pillars of salt and a forty-day rain. i am returned. the clotted streets are dark, perfecting their piracy. how long's it been? i lived between the midget joys of militants, refusing bread, bureaucracy, and regulation gentleness. indecision in a borrowed dress: *i can't go on - - - i'll go on.* rage's silk insistence, take a hammer to the printing press. syndromal, votive mood tonight. addicts lounge in languorous camp, long limbs like compass needles. sickly, magnetised and limping. surrender is also a choice, you know? deliberate as drinking. the safe fatigue of the working week, and stroking a dog with forger's ears. but where *were* you? at the laying out and the winding in. blame-wounded. obituaries and butcher's shops, the bones we boil for glue. girls, boys. boy, whose head a brazen drum. our music is the misfit friction made from striking him. again, again. give my head peace. poet, poetry. you cherry-pick my brittle dead, pose with your foot in their chalky haunches. you were not there. this pain is meaning without language, is language without thought. is dyslexia, unmitigated pig iron, the demotic of exhaustion, garbled, trimmed from the tongue. >> *what do you think?* tragedy is a dunce-rhythm nobody grooves to. lyre. lyra. lioness. our griefs are ours, each to her own. mine flies free, kite caught wayward by the wrist. or takes shape slowly, like glass being blown.

It's true, I did tell that girl to fuck off. I should have done it sooner – it felt very liberating. This came at the end of a long, aggravating day, and I might call it symptomatic of my ongoing crisis of faith in both poetry and in London's self-appointed Poetry Community. I might also call it part of a wider discomfort, something nebulous and creeping that I feel about the world. For a while now things haven't been right. When things aren't right then I tend to withdraw. I was recently described as being "militantly analogue". Which isn't a compliment.

I'm sick of it, though, this culture of compulsory visibility. I'm sick of the implied ethical imperative contained within the claims of identity politics to visibility as an exemplary radical platform. I'm with Glissant and "opacity", the Invisible Committee and their "*éthico-affinitaire*".[1] Identarianism is a shitty right-wing import, toxic to all forms of affective solidarity. What I'm striving for is that species of unquantifiable alterity; a diversity that exceeds any attempt to impose categories of identifiable difference; that resists the hierarchies such absolute othering implies. Radical political claims shouldn't depend upon rendering identities visible, get me? In other words, I'm sick of online spaces that demand a continuous, coherent performance of self, of self as poet, of self's stance, self's posture, self's politics and position. "Woke" for likes. It isn't just that I value my privacy, although I do, it's also that identity itself has been appropriated for the purposes of control by the agents of neoliberal digital surveillance. And I don't want to be data. I don't want to be a target demographic. I don't want to be reduced to an algorithm, advertised at. I especially do not want to dwell in a flat nuance-less echo chamber of my own preconceived ideas and opinions. I aspire to a state of sensitised and fiercely vigilant ignorance, alert to all I do not know, and part of a broader communal questioning. Not just networked, but actually *connected*, in a way our current conception of social media doesn't account for. Nor our current conception of poetry.

In poetry, compulsory visibility is intimately related to the notion of "accessibility", specifically, to the notion of accessibility constructed as some kind of absolute and unassailable moral category. Yuck. Demanding that individual creative projects are rendered accessible somewhat disingenuously ignores the element of craft in *all* poetry, whether written by Attila the Stockbroker or J. H. sodding Prynne. It asks we take poetry as speech, and assumes that this speech originates within a coherent, confessive, lyric "I". It also cunningly avoids engaging with the deep systemic and structural inequalities inherent in the publication and transmission of poetry, or indeed in language itself. Make no mistake, to be poor, to be "other", is to be failed by language, by the sterile functionality of commonplace language encounters, their bland bureaucracies, their invisibilising rhetorics, their dehumanising slang. We can't fight what besets us with the oppressor's words and phrases. It is no longer enough to say, "I am cold, I am hungry". Those words have lost their meaning, their ability to shock people into awareness. To expose what ordinary language obscures requires strangeness and hybridity; new phrases, new ways of saying, specifically deployed to retune attention towards human suffering.

It's not enough to keep peddling that dead confessive self, either. And I speak as someone whose work is positively infested with the lyric "I". I'd like to think, though, that when I write about Travellerness or Irishness or Queerness, I'm attempting to do more than make some kind of shitty, pretentious gesture towards universality. I'd like to think I'm doing more than directing my readers towards a single, monolithic interpretation of meaning. I'm not about originating insights from a position of individual exceptionalism and/or privileged interiority. I don't want to be an ambassador apologist for any group, but I do want to signal my participation and complicity in the wider world. My readers' too. How *does* a poem negotiate between the pain felt by an individual and the collective radical engagement such an individual demands? I don't know. I do know that after the murder of journalist Lyra McKee by the NIRA in Derry earlier this year I was asked repeatedly if I would write something. These requests became quite forceful, no longer "Will you write something?", more "Why haven't you written anything?" And this was the context to my fuck off moment. It was a fuck off of *You are not entitled to my pain*, and a fuck off of *I am not entitled to the pain of others*.

Poetry is not entitled, either. Or, it shouldn't get to pick and choose its scenes of ethical engagement in isolated moments of reactionary lyric flux. And if that's what poetry is doing, if that's what we're doing as poets, then it/we are failing.

So I'm not writing a poem about the death of Lyra McKee. I'm not writing a poem about the "renewed hostilities" in the north of Ireland. Just because it's expected of me, because it's part of my "persona". I'm writing a poem about grief and grieving and the several springs of that grief. And I'm writing about the complacency and indifference with which that grief has traditionally been treated by literary communities in the UK. And I'm writing about compromise and complicity. I'm writing about language's need to escape into strangeness in frantic response to the distortional stresses of trauma. I'm writing about voyeurism. I'm writing about depression and addiction, and the loss of my oldest friend. I'm writing about how we write and work around that loss and all the other losses that we hold and feel in common. There's an "I" and an "us" and a "them" and a "you". And sometimes there's no way to tell them apart. These categories become conflated and confused, transgressed across multiple categories of othered belonging. It's a lamentation and an accusation. It's us. It's everything.

1   Édouard Glissant was a French writer, poet, philosopher and literary critic from Martinique. In his book *Poetics of Relation*, he argues for "the right to opacity that is not enclosure within an impenetrable autarchy but subsistence within an irreducible singularity. Opacities can coexist and converge, weaving fabrics. To understand these truly one must focus on the texture of the weave and not on the nature of its components." Édouard Glissant, *Poetics of Relation*, trans. Betsy Wing (Ann Arbor: University of Michigan Press, 1997), p.190. The "Invisible Committee" is the collective nom de plume of a French anarchist cooperative, who have published numerous works of anti-capitalist and anti-state literature. Best known of these is *The Coming Insurrection* (Los Angeles: Semiotext(e), 2009).

FICTION

SHIFTING SANDS

This is where the river once ran. My brother Laurie remembers it as being ice cold, racing with meltwater from mountain snows. Back then, he says, you had to wade across, boots slung by their laces from your neck as your toes turned blue.

Today, the plain is broad and dry. Driftwood still clumps in memory of the fish and other life that sheltered in its shade. Laurie and I break some up to carry with us. It'll burn well if we have the chance to make a fire.

The sand dunes wait ahead, their cinnamon peaks and falls vivid against the dawn sky. After so many months of travelling towards their haze, it's strange that they're almost within our reach.

But the dunes conceal their own threats.

"We need to move fast," Laurie says, as if Alfred and I need reminding. By mid-morning, the winds will have risen and sun will sear the land.

Before the Internet crashed, over a year ago, stories were already filtering back. Worst was the footage shot on smart-phones, showing the before and after of the winds.

The theories I've read and discarded as nonsense rattle through my mind. Dread slides into my gut just thinking that. It's exactly what these winds do – rattle through the mind, eroding memory and erasing personality.

Windstruck, people called it on social media. #windstruck #grief

Laurie hands out foil-wrapped protein bars. I notice he eats only half of his portion. Our supplies must be getting low again.

"Look, Aunt Lutta!" Alfred points to rabbit tracks. "Bet they can survive anything."

"Anything but coyotes," I say. "Did you hear the howls last night?"

Alfred shrugs. He's learnt to sleep through almost anything.

The sands, when we get to them, show evidence of those who've attempted to cross before – an abandoned sleigh here, a dropped backpack there. No footprints though. No bones. The winds erase or cover those each day.

"Wait here with Lutta," Laurie tells Alfred. He strides on down the slope and stoops over the polka-dot fabric of a backpack. I hear the sound of a zip and Laurie raises an arm, brandishing a small object triumphantly. He exclaims in jubilation: "Fruit!"

Laurie clambers up the dune where the sand rises to meet the far side of the wind-sculpted hill Alfred and I stand on. We hurry to meet him. Each step sinks, creating miniature collapses that swallow our feet and slow our progress.

"Walk in my footprints, Alfred," I say.

I watch him tread where the sand has been packed down a little by my weight. Even inside his hiking boots, his feet look tiny. He's slight for his age, small and dark. Taking after his mum, Agati.

I remember being his age, and younger, on the family walks we did then for fun, to get "fresh air", to fill the weekend hours and "build up an appetite". I remember wellington boots that gaped around my shins and liberated me to stomp in puddles; hoods worn only to prevent rainwater spilling into our eyes, when it was an inconvenience, not danger and not pain.

We reach Laurie and he opens the backpack to show us. The smell of rot is cloying but the apples inside appear edible, if wizened. It's the first tree-grown fruit we've seen in months.

"Why do you think they left it?" Alfred asks. "What happened to them?"

Laurie shrugs, avoiding his son's eyes and mine. "Windstruck, maybe." He glances around at the once verdant landscape, and at the mountains ahead.

Laurie zips the polka-dot backpack closed and shoulders it above his own. There's no time to taste our bounty, although our stomachs growl. The day glitters around us, mica in the sand catching the light and throwing it at us like a coppery-gold warning. The sun climbs the sky faster than we can scale the dunes.

"Come on. The winds will be here soon."

"Look." Alfred points.

There's movement in the fold between two dunes: something more sand-coloured, more like the yellowish sand from beaches, than the red sand we walk on.

A lone coyote.

Alfred dashes down the slope, curiosity releasing a burst of energy. The coyote doesn't slink off as it should – it remains where it is, head bobbing as though smelling the air as my nephew approaches.

Something's not right.

Alfred hunkers low beside the animal. My brother and I join him. The coyote sits, tongue lolling. I don't see an injury apart from a tear in its left ear, but that scar appears old. The animal looks confused, as though it's forgotten what we are, why it should attack us, or run away.

"Windstruck," I say. "Poor thing."

Skin-covered bones show through bald patches in the tawny fur.

"Can we give her water, Dad?" Alfred asks. "Please?"

Laurie puts one hand on his shoulder. "We barely have enough for ourselves. It's already a goner, mate. Sorry."

Alfred scowls. "What, so we should just leave her here to die? Like we did Mum? You don't care about anyone but yourself!"

The coyote flinches, but doesn't move away.

"Alfred, we didn't leave Agati to … I would never leave your mum to die. I needed to keep you safe." The anguish in my brother's voice is enough to quiet us all. "She may be ahead of us yet," he murmurs.

I wonder if he believes his words.

Something in the light changes. The faintest breeze weaves through the air.

"Dig!" Laurie shouts. He throws off his backpacks and falls to his knees, clawing at the sand. Alfred and I shovel frantically, excavating palmful after palmful. My fingernails tear and my skin splits, but none of that matters.

The coyote has disappeared.

We hear a terrible throaty groan that sounds almost human.

"Down!" My brother urges us into the ditch. Light is blotted out as he flings himself on top, shielding us.

I screw my eyes up tight.

The wind has exhausted itself, for now. When all falls silent, I push at my brother. He is a dead weight, but I feel his breathing against my spine.

I push harder and he topples onto one side as I edge out from underneath him. I help Alfred scramble upright.

"OK?"

Alfred nods without speaking, eyes fixed on his dad's slumped form.

I manoeuvre Laurie into a sitting position. He blinks at me, his expression vacant.

"Laurie?" I hear the waver in my voice.

Sand cakes his back and his greying blond hair is tufted at odd angles from where the winds hit him.

"Is he ...?" Alfred begins. He bites his lower lip.

"He'll be fine," I say.

Alfred nudges against his dad like a cat, rubbing his head against his back and stomach.

I feed Laurie an apple, cutting off chunks and slipping the pieces between his lips until some reflex is prompted and he chews.

Relief surges through me. Surely that's a good sign.

I think about the videos I saw online of people filming their windstruck families. Some would zoom in right up to their relatives' faces, so their empty eyes filled the screen.

Whatever language they used, they all said the same thing: *Don't come here. It's dangerous. You'll lose those you love.*

Stay away.

I pull Laurie up and he stands, swaying. When I tug his arm, he shuffles one foot in front of the other.

Alfred stares at him, afraid.

"He's still your dad," I say, trying to sound confident. I drag on Laurie's backpack over my own and pass Alfred the one with the apples. "Let's go."

The rhythm of walking settles in, pushing up and down the dunes towards the mountains.

Perhaps the blankness is temporary, I tell myself. Perhaps by nightfall, Laurie will have returned to us.

Darkness descends before we reach the foothills. I select a space at the base of a dune and we set up camp. My nephew and brother curl beside me in their sleepsacks, each with a backpack as a pillow. Laurie's eyes glint worriedly in the fading light, but I stroke his hair until they close.

In the night the coyotes come, not the bewildered creature we met earlier, but hungry, alert canines that whine and yap to each other as though plotting their attack. I rouse Alfred and we clap our hands and shout, making as much noise as possible. Laurie adds screeches to the mix, though whether from fright or solidarity I can't tell.

The coyotes melt into the darkness. There's easier prey to be had in this shifting landscape.

When I wake again, it's morning.

A woman squats a foot or two away, eyes narrowed as though she's assessing me. I sit up and try to shoot to my feet, but Laurie and Alfred are lying across my legs, one angled from the right, the other from the left.

"Reckon they've hemmed you to the sand," the stranger comments. Her voice rasps. I follow her gaze to Laurie's face and see that he's awake, blinking anxiously.

"Windstruck, hmm?" the woman says. "The fear's something – better than emptiness."

She unzips the backpack at her feet and retrieves a wrinkled apple. Inwardly I swear.

"That's ours!"

She turns the apple in her hand and grins. "Is it, though? I found it unattended here in the sand. Could have been anyone's. What corpse did you rob it from?"

I shrug, unable to argue. I nudge Alfred so he stirs, rubbing his face.

The woman lobs me the apple, and, despite myself, I flinch as it flies past. Alfred scrabbles after it.

The woman laughs. "What a good boy your son is!"

The statement jolts through me. There's no way she could know about Jacob.

I glower at the woman. She's no taller than me, but stockier, with her bare arms strung with lean muscle. There's a hardness to her expression even in laughter that makes my stomach tense.

"Circumstances change a person," she says as though she's read my thoughts. "I like to think I'm a reasonable person.

Three of you, one of me. Let's split the apples between us. A quarter each."

Again, I can't think of an argument. "All right," I agree. "But we keep the backpack."

The woman shrugs. "Looks like you've got more than enough to lug, but sure. Why not?"

She spreads the apples across the sand, counting. For a second our surroundings and the orbs of fruit remind me of playing boules on a beach.

I press the memory away.

A quarter of the apples amounts to the grand sum of eight each, some of which are already threatening decay. The woman hands me the backpack laden with our twenty-four, and stuffs hers into her own bag. It's bulging and I wonder what else she has in there.

I take Laurie's boots off and shake out the sand, then remove his socks too, checking for any sores. Laurie watches me intently, frowning, but doesn't stop me, or try to help.

His feet don't smell great, but they're fine.

"Do yours, Alfred," I say as I wrestle Laurie's socks and boots on again and tend to my own feet.

The woman eyes us, but doesn't say anything.

"Right." I stand up and reach for Laurie's hands. "Let's get going."

We're walking in the same direction so there's no reason to separate from the woman other than the distrust churning beneath my skin.

"Wait," Alfred says, and he turns and stares.

I turn too, moving Laurie so that the three of us face the way we've come, over the undulating topography of red sand. Shadows brim in every hollow, like rainwater used to fill riverbeds and create puddles from holes. The sun has painted everything saffron and indigo. I wore a skirt in those colours when I was small – it swept about me like the morning sky whenever I danced or ran.

The woman doesn't pause. She strides onwards, barely slowing her pace.

Travelling as fast as we're able with Laurie, we manage to keep her in our sights.

*

We've crossed most of the foothills by evening.

At last the woman comes to a halt and we catch up. "We'll stay here tonight. It's too dry for a fire – this scrubland would catch in an instant," she says. "I'll take first watch, then you."

I nod, even though I won't dare sleep with her awake, and I suspect she feels the same about me even if she is stronger, fiercer.

I slice up another apple, feeding it to Laurie piece by piece. He looks at me as he eats, as if trying to puzzle something out.

I save the seeds, wrapping them in a page torn from the book *Silent Spring* by Rachel Carson. I run my thumb over a paragraph: *The apple trees were coming into bloom, but no bees droned among the blossoms, so there was no pollination and there would be no fruit.*

"I'm Lutta, your sister," I tell Laurie softly, not wanting the woman to hear. "That's Alfred, your boy. We'll keep you safe, love. You kept us from harm all this time. Now we'll keep you."

My words are a murmur threading the air. They comfort me as much as him, I think.

I reach into the polka-dot backpack with the apples. My hand catches on something so light it has almost no weight. I remove the object from the bag and stare at it, startled by its orange plastic.

Then I laugh. "Look at that, Laurie. A comb! Just like Mum used to have." Laurie's head quivers on his neck, face slack. I move closer to him and run my hand over his scalp.

One sweep after another, I tame his hair, gently easing the knots free without pulling. He sits motionless for a few moments, and then catches my hand. "My sister," he says, and I smile.

"Yes, me, your kid sister, here to annoy you like always." I touch his brow. "We made it across the dunes, Laurie. We're safe and sound."

He moves so suddenly I jerk backwards. His face contorts with distress. "Not safe," he screeches. "Not safe, not safe!" His words fracture into a yowl.

Alfred jolts upright.

I enfold Laurie in my arms and rock him, holding him until his wailing subsides into moans.

"OK, not safe, but we're across the sand. Next we have to find a path over the mountains."

He shakes his head vigorously. "No, no," he mumbles.

I see the insistence in his eyes.

"Not the mountains?" I ask, and he glares, shaking his head even more vehemently.

"OK, yes to the mountains?" I suggest, feeling as though we're playing some weird game of charades.

He nods, panting.

"What was the no for then?" Alfred asks.

"Yes to the mountain ..." I think aloud. "But no to ... no to over."

Laurie nods again.

"Not over ... but –" I begin.

"If we can't go over," the woman interjects, "we'll have to go through."

* * * * *

That day at the beach in the south of France, I remember the sound of boules striking each other with light, wooden clunks. I was six years old. My indigo-and-saffron skirt wafted around my skinny legs; my feet danced in glittering water where silvery fish darted. The sun was so bright that when I looked up the sky was all white and blue. Nearby, the grown-ups were talking about climate change: "There must be something to be done."

One memory segues into another, the next of a beach in the years after Alfred and Jacob were born.

No one was paddling, because the water was already toxic. I was keeping an eye on the kids while Agati talked about her work at Plymouth University.

"Hard to believe such good intentions led to this," she said, indicating the sludgy water. Dead fish glimmered in the shallows. "The decades of work by Dr Cair have resulted in the worst possible outcome for us all."

Hazel Cair was one of Agati's colleagues.

"What do you mean? What was she working on?"

"An enzyme that devours plastic," Agati said. "Somehow word got out when testing was still underway. The extremist wing of an environmental group broke into the lab. They poured gallons of the stuff into the oceans."

"But wasn't that the goal?"

"It wasn't ready," she said, shaking her head. I'd never seen her look afraid before. "It devours plastic as expected, but in the process a chemical by-product is released, turning the water acidic. Within months, it's likely marine life will be extinct."

"Stop him!" Laurie cried out, panic in his voice.

My first thought was Jacob, but it was little Alfred, arms fluttering for balance as he tottered towards the light glinting on sluggish waves. I ran after my nephew and swung him into my arms.

Alfred's screams were not because he was thwarted in his goal to touch that sea, or due to the shock of being hoisted into the air, but because a wave splashed out like a tendril and caught his bare golden leg.

The crimson scar of that burn still shows faintly today.

✳ ✳ ✳ ✳ ✳

I wake to a sound like bone cracking. The sun is already rising. The woman has let me sleep the night through.

She is kneeling over something small and furred that hangs limp in her hands. A rabbit.

"Windstruck," she says when she sees me watching. "Hopped right in front of me. That'll be tonight's dinner."

I turn to see Alfred yawning and stretching. Beside him, Laurie is out of his sleepsack. He's fumbling with his bootlaces, but it's clear he can't work out how to loosen them. He's breathing heavily with frustration.

I crouch beside him. "Let me do that," I offer as though I'm just being polite.

He sits back as I undo the laces and slide the boots off his feet, followed by his socks. A hole is forming in the heel of one. I show him, sticking my thumb through.

The woman leans over us. "What are you checking for?"

"Anything that could become a blister or worse," I say. "Feet are our most important survival tool. If they go bad, we're stuffed."

I finish checking Laurie's feet and my own, making sure Alfred's done his too.

At last we're ready to leave.

✳

The mountains loom above us, rocky crowns disappearing into the glistening sky. I expect to spend days seeking the entrance, but before the morning has passed, the woman leads us directly to a fissure. I don't ask how she knows so precisely what she's looking for but I see a flicker of relief ruffle the usual grimness of her expression. It's as though someone made a promise and didn't let her down when it mattered most.

She has more water left than us and shares it. At her urging we add drops of purifier and protein powder. She nods, satisfied, as Alfred grimaces but swigs the mixture.

For the first time I wonder who she's missing. We've all lost people.

In other ways, the woman seems less prepared than us. Laurie, Alfred and I each have a battery-powered head torch in our packs. I hand her Laurie's to wear, holding myself back from asking how she'd expected to navigate her passage through the caves without light.

She gestures to us to linger in the shadow of a rocky outcrop. We stand silently, waiting. I feel as though we're predators seeking prey, but it's more likely we're the quarry.

Nothing moves. The woman motions for us to approach the fissure. "Better cautious than dead."

Alfred stops suddenly, staring behind us into the distance.

"What is it?" I whirl around, my heart palpitating in my chest.

A skinny coyote trots towards us. The tear in the left ear shows it's the same one we met before the winds got Laurie.

"Here, Peggy, good girl." Alfred rumples her fur. She doesn't show any aggression, only a mild bemusement as though she's certain she knows my nephew from somewhere but isn't sure how.

"Good girl, Peggy."

The woman frowns. "Care to explain?"

I shrug. "The coyote's windstruck." I touch Alfred's shoulder. "She can't come with us. She's not a pet."

"But she'll die if we leave her."

I recognise the obstinate set of his lower lip. Jacob used to make that face before a full-on tantrum.

My boy. He'd have wanted to save the coyote too. We've already lost so much. I glance at my brother, and shrug again.

"If you bring her into the caves and she goes missing, we're not launching a search party. Got it?"

"Got it."

According to the longitude and latitude we've each memorised, the mountains shelter the entrance to a cloud forest more self-contained than any other on this continent. Others are dotted throughout the world. These ecosystems depend not on rain but on water filtered by rock. It seeps from caves and dampens the mossy ground before evaporating into clouds.

The air will be quenching and pure, the weather entirely localised. A microclimate unsullied by the toxin ravaging the oceans and poisoning rainfall.

My heart races at the thought.

* * * * *

Agati's work at Plymouth University meant her circle of acquaintance mainly comprised people with niche obsessions. If you asked the right question it was like discovering a freshwater spring – riches bubbled to the surface.

One of her colleagues worked in earth sciences: "Geology," he translated. "I specialise in seismology. It's been a busy time. We've just sent a machine to Mars that will discover whether the planet has quakes. You can see from the surface that there were in the past, but understanding the current conditions will help us deduce the planet's make-up. We don't even know whether it's solid or liquid!"

His excitement was as contagious as a small child's.

It was too late, though – too late to think of sending humans to Mars and establishing colonies on that red planet.

Our own small planet was already losing its greens and blues.

Agati received the coordinates to the cloud forest from a colleague, just days after the universities disintegrated.

"Share sparingly," she warned me. "The forest can only sustain a fraction of the population. This is about survival."

She also said that false coordinates were appearing across the Internet. "That should buy us some time."

*

Guests at Laurie and Agati's parties often asked what I did. I watched their polite interest fade when I said full-time mum. I took to adding that I also volunteered at Beavers, omitting the fact that Jacob's health issues meant that was the proviso on which they'd let him join.

＊ ＊ ＊ ＊ ＊

Jacob would have loved the caves. That's what I think as we step inside. The interior is as indigo as a bruise; our head torches paint the route ahead gold.

Peggy whines as the darkness closes over us. I hear my brother whimper too.

"It's OK," Alfred whispers. "I'll look after you." I think he's speaking to the coyote, but Laurie's breathing steadies beside me.

A smell gnaws at my nostrils – something muddy and faintly acrid. A subtle, relentless clicking noise rises from the fathoms of the caves. Clicking and dripping and rustling. I move my head, trying to see.

The woman puts her hand on my arm. "Ignorance might be bliss, eh?" she comments, a fraction later than might have helped.

A heaving mass of cockroaches clamber over one another's bodies. They gleam amber and bronze in the torchlight. Bat guano is piled in clotted heaps, and it's on this that they're feasting. The coyote snaps at the writhing mass I've illuminated.

"Eat them up, Peggy," Alfred says. "Good girl. That's it."

Above us, bats flit among tooth-like rock formations. A snicker of claws on stone announces the presence of a spool of rats.

"Don't touch anything, Alfred," I hiss.

The woman laughs. "Like we haven't all been trying our hardest not to touch anything since this nightmare began."

We trudge through the slippery tunnels, trying not to crush cockroaches when we reach out our bare hands for balance. The number of beetles thins as we leave the entrance behind and the stench of bat guano lessens. Soon the only sound is our own panting and shuffling, and a quiet, continual dripping of water.

After several hours, Alfred's footsteps falter and I see him sway. "We need to rest," I say, letting go of Laurie's hand to grab Alfred's shoulders. He tilts into me, eyelids fluttering.

The woman turns, irritated, but her face softens when she sees his exhaustion.

"OK." She ushers us behind a large, flattish rock like a screen or a shield.

I build a fire from the wood we gathered at the dry riverbed. The woman watches and I feel her surprise.

"Beavers," I say, but she doesn't understand what I mean.

"My son," I add, swallowing. "I went with him to Beavers – a club for kids where they learn stuff like …" I gesture to the flames, unable to say more.

The woman nods. "What happened to him?"

"He was … he was on various medications. Insulin for diabetes. Clonazepam for epilepsy, among others."

"Unlucky," she says.

I'm glad she doesn't expect me to explain the impossibility of getting enough of the drugs; describe Jacob's gradual decline. I marked his grave with a cairn of rocks, not trusting that the tree we buried him beneath will still be standing when we return.

It's only now, I realise, that I'm beginning to accept how unlikely it is that we'll go home.

The coyote's ragged ear twitches as Alfred sings, but she lies quiet and obedient in the fire's glow. "A sailor went to sea sea sea, to see what he could see see see, but all that he could see see see, was the bottom of the deep blue sea sea sea."

Jacob taught Alfred that clapping game. As the elder of the two by a little over a year, he felt it was his duty to pass on as much knowledge as possible to his cousin.

"Poor sailor," Alfred says, kissing his fist and touching it to the coyote's nose so she licks the knuckles. "He must've drowned, mustn't he, Aunt Lutta? Otherwise, how could he have seen the *bottom* of the sea?"

"That's right, Alfred," I say, dragging his sleepsack from his bag. "Come on, get comfy and shut your eyes. I'll wake you in the morning."

Jacob had been the one who unravelled the morbidity of the children's rhyme. As soon as he'd learnt to talk he'd done the same with every fairy tale I told him. It bothered me at the time, but now I think, *Smart kid*. That clarity, his instinct to unpick what he was told, could have kept him safe.

If he'd been luckier.

I cup my palm against my brother's face. He leans into it.

"Sleep time, Laurie," I tell him, and he nods, lying down.

Definitely improving, I tell myself. Definitely comprehends what I say.

* * * * *

The day the power died, people panicked. Tap water was already unsafe to consume and the supermarkets had been emptied, first by preppers and then by looters. Even the streets of our small city were crowded with people shouting and crying.

We stayed indoors, keeping the kids distracted with games of Monopoly while Laurie went through the house, making sure we hadn't missed anything we might need.

A loud bang made Jacob jump.

"Stay away from the window," I told him.

"Why? What's happening out there?"

"Nothing," I lied. "Just a few grown-ups being silly."

We'd had the coordinates for over a week by then. I'd made us hang on while I tried to stockpile as much of Jacob's medication as I could.

We were all in the living room when Agati got a text message. She grabbed Laurie's arm and pulled him into the hallway, out of sight.

"Stay here," I told Jacob and Alfred, and followed them into the hall.

"I need to swing by the university and help Hazel," Agati said. "If I'm not back by midnight, head out. I'll catch you up."

Laurie lowered his head and then pulled her into a tight hug, speaking softly into her ear.

"Mum, please don't go," Alfred begged, bursting past me. He flung his arms around her.

"I'll be back before you know it," she promised, bending down and kissing the tears streaming down his face. "You won't even know I'm gone."

After she left, we waited for two days. By that time, buildings on our street had begun to collapse in flames.

"We have to go," I said. "It isn't safe here now."

"Agati –" Laurie began.

"Agati knows she missed our deadline," I told him, even though it made me feel sick inside. "She'd have set out, wouldn't she?"

He looked at me and nodded, blinking hard. "OK, get the boys. Tell them it's time."

That was more than eighteen months ago.

＊ ＊ ＊ ＊ ＊

In the indigo darkness, days and nights become no more than an idea.

The light from our torches is diminishing. We take turns to switch one on so the batteries from the other two will last a little longer. The glow they cast now is less gold than orange, and even that is weakening.

We come to a cavern where pools have formed in dips on the rock floor. We've grown so accustomed to regarding water as a threat that my first thought is danger. How can I get Laurie and Alfred through without anyone being burnt?

The coyote pushes forward.

"Peggy, no!" Alfred cries as I grab his shoulders to prevent him following.

The animal crouches, tongue lapping with a sound that resonates around the space.

She isn't recoiling in pain.

The woman and I exchange glances. "Hang on," she says, and walks to the nearest pool. With extreme care, she dips a small bottle into the water, rights it and adds violet powder. I stare, not sure what I'm looking for as the liquid changes colour from pale purple to blue.

The woman exhales loudly. "We can drink it. We'll need to add purifier solution to be sure, but it's potable."

I gape, and then grin. Laurie blinks and I hug him. "The water's safe, Laurie. Agati's directions were right. We must be getting near."

Hours later I wake to a darkness that's no longer absolute. On the edges of my vision, gold discs glint in pairs. Eyes.

The woman places a hand on my arm. She sits beside me, keeping watch. "I see them too. Go to sleep. I'll wake you if there's trouble."

When we rise at what may be morning, the coyote is sniffing the air where I saw the eyes. I direct the fading torch beam at her paws and see hoofprints in the dust.

"Ungulates," the woman says, and I nod.

"We must be getting close," I say, for the second time, feeling my blood jump in my veins.

We emerge in a half-light that I interpret as daybreak, dazzled and blinking in its unfamiliar brilliance. Alfred and his coyote dart ahead before I can caution them.

I identify with their elation. It's like entering paradise. The woman whose name I've never asked grasps my hand, eyes shining.

A broad bowl of a valley sweeps before us, ringed by mountains and tousled with trees. Beneath a canopy of mist, leaves of emerald, viridian and the brightest spring hues shiver in the air. Fresh, earthy aromas sing through to my lungs, lightening every blood cell they pass over and ringing up to my brain.

Sounds, too, clamour for attention – layers of birdsong, a crescendo of insect cries, animal calls, rustles and woodland creaks. Beneath it chimes the tumult of water falling.

I feel for the twist of paper in my pocket, bulging with the apple seeds I've collected.

Laurie stumbles past me, face contorted in a way I don't recognise. "Agati," he croaks.

I look, but can't see his wife, or anyone, in the landscape ahead. The view is tangled with greenery that represents proof of life, something we've not seen for what feels like an eternity, but anything more is hidden by its abundance.

Then I understand. The expression my brother wears is one of hope.

NON-FICTION

THE KUSI

JEAN MCNEIL

At nine in the morning it is already thirty degrees. The heat is a curtain that must be pushed aside to get beyond, to some cool, air-conditioned realm where everyone makes rational decisions and loves people who are good for them.

My partner/boyfriend/lover (all these terms sound wrong) and I sit in the ice cream parlour. There are actually three in what is otherwise a small African village. Today we are at Andrea's. He is a Neapolitan whose ex-girlfriend left him for a local guy and set up a rival, and possibly better, ice cream business charging London prices for tubs of *stracciatella* down the road, igniting an African-village version of the Ice Cream Wars.

Our beach is frequently listed as the "no. 2 beach in Africa"; no one seems to know the identity of no. 1 – Clifton in Cape Town perhaps, or Vamizi in Mozambique. But this year tourism is down. Terrorism is one reason – Al-Shabaab has mounted attacks across the border recently, and despite the Kenyan government's best efforts to sit on the stories they have made the news, spooking the Americans and Brits who, unlike the hardier Italians, have shunned the coast.

"It will come back," he says. He means tourism.

"Somalia is a hundred kilometres from here," I argue. "Somalia is not going away."

"People's memories are short," he counters. "Once six months have gone by and there's been no news, they'll come back. They always come back."

He should know; he has weathered many peaks and troughs on the coast. He's been coming here ever since he was a reedy six-year-old boy. He is of this country, despite his Scottish surname and the fume of rectitude that cloaks his lanky frame. His uncle constructed the first proper house on the beach in the days when elephant walked from the forest to bathe in the waters and Sykes monkeys trapezed unimpeded through the branches of the casuarina and mbambakofi trees. That was a long time ago, though, and now the community consists of locals farming the sandy soil of the backlands while builders of super-yachts and German aristocracy hog the beachfront. Most worrying is a new development, almost certainly funded by shady money, to build a sixty-storey hotel – an insane project which will ruin the natural environment and maybe even the community. The despoliations hitting our village come so thick and fast it's impossible to keep count of let alone fight them.

We finish our *gelato* (me: passion fruit; him: hazelnut), surrounded by close-shaven Italian men. Their signet rings clink against espresso cups, producing a Tibetan-prayer-bell-like sound. Soon I must return to the northern hemisphere. We will be parted for three months and the air between us has begun to curdle. Each time I return to London I have to tear myself away. There is an original power in the landscape here, in this northern arc of the Indian Ocean, with its hectares of pristine mangroves, a ruined Swahili city and dugongs nosing through kelp metres from where we sit eating *gelato*. But also the Indian Ocean coast really is a separate dimension from the rest of my life. Moving between the two I feel more than displaced, as if I have lost the skill for perceiving each reality on its own terms and must learn it again.

"You'll come back," he says, spooning his ice cream thoughtfully into his mouth. "At Christmas."

Yes, I think, I will always come back here. It has me under its spell. Some places do that to us, it seems – we are glamoured by them. But also I think my fascination with this place is an impersonal attempt to regain some perspective, not on myself but on my species, to ground myself in an original enchantment.

There are two seasons on the coast: wet and slightly less wet, hot and slightly less hot. The kusi monsoon blows from April until September, winter on this latitude, bringing squalls of urgent, enveloping rain. The kaskazi is the summer monsoon, arriving in time for Christmas and departing the coast around Easter.

Summer brings salad days; hotels at full capacity, Neapolitans with their Bain de Soleil tans thronged around the bar at the Come Back Club, a calm ocean in which trapezoid-shaped sand bars loll in jade waters. During the kusi, however, days can be cooler than in London or Paris and at night the temperature can dip to twenty degrees, a locally Arctic number that has people reaching for their feather jackets and knitted hats.

Lately the seasons have started to blur. The swing season, when the wind pauses on its hinge, is called the matalai. "The weather is changing," says Mukenka – of whom more later. "Everywhere this is what the elders say. They look at the sky and no longer recognise what they see there."

In the kaskazi the beach's peach-hued sands are pristine, but in the squall days of the kusi it becomes coated with plastics from all corners of the Indian Ocean. Its cargo of severed doll's limbs last seen in Perth, Australia, or toothbrushes last used to scrub a quarry peasant's molars in Madagascar, lie entangled with clots of seaweed that somehow all look like Russia in outline.

Other changes have made themselves felt in this small coastal community of late: rumours of a Chinese mega-port to be built at Lamu up the coast, near the Somali border. Everyone knows what that will mean: the mauling of mangroves and cancelling of sandbars. Dugongs and whale sharks will die. Newcomers are also settling in the community – Maasai, mostly, driven from their pasturelands by a variety of factors, including climate-change-induced drought. From the sea we are assailed by Tanzanian fishermen, who journey across the maritime border illegally in slim *ngalawas* because in Tanzania they have dynamited all the fish from the ocean.

In the past few years Kenya has withstood a volatile see-saw of drought and flood. Neither is particularly new to this wedge-shaped country, home to fifty million people, and which has one of the fastest population growth rates in the world. But in April 2018 a savage drought, the worst in the region in two thousand years and which had seen no rain fall in six months in some areas of the country, was abruptly cancelled by flooding that displaced thousands.

Extreme weather has begun to finger our peninsula, sandwiched between the ocean and a saltwater creek fringed with dense mangroves. The community is home to three conservation organisations and a protected pocket of the tropical lowland forest that used to stretch unbroken from Somalia to Mozambique. Turtles are regularly rescued and rehabilitated, mambas are harvested for their venom at the snake farm so that bite victims around the world have a chance of survival, the coral gardens where we snorkel and which are home to a fearsomely grumpy moray eel we call Twiga (giraffe in Swahili) are still relatively healthy; even the conniving Sykes monkeys are protected by law.

But peninsulas are fragile environments. The liminal nature of the peninsula is present in its name, derived from the Latin *paena* (almost) and *insula* (island): these almost-islands are jumping-off points, polygamously wedded to sea and land. For some time the skies haven't looked right to the elders here, either. "It's strange, strange weather," my partner says, sitting on the *baraza* (sofa) from where he has a commanding view of an empty ocean.

We have no television or wi-fi in the house and while watching films on DVDs is theoretically possible, the CD reader's USB port has long ago rusted into disuse (the coastal climate knocks electronics dead), so the skies are our entertainment system. I am mesmerised by the curtailed twilights of the tropics, by the violet commas of evening cloud, the shuffling of White-browed coucal in the shrubbery, sorties of Mosque swallows, and the Southern Cross and Pleiades tacking themselves above the horizon as night advances at 1,300 kilometres an hour – the speed at which we hurtle around on the planet's tropical belt. Sometimes I try to visualise it: us, figures plastered to a merry-go-round in a children's park, or one of those NASA centrifuges which lasso astronauts around and around until their gums peel away from their teeth. The planet is speeding up. Yes, that's it. A quickening.

I meet Dale at Ocean Sports, the local expat hangout half a kilometre along the beach from our house. All sorts of fascinating flotsam wash up there: a Ugandan doctor on holiday with his family, a fashion designer from London, Arab women from some Gulf state who sit in the sun in full abayas wearing pink and green Havaianas on their perfectly pedicured feet.

Dale is a fisheries expert who had been working at the FAO. Like many of his veteran NGO brethren, Dale long ago ceased to be American. The accent remains, as does the white skin he cannot shed, but after fifteen years in Africa he has become an interstitial creature. He knows it: he tells me he has fallen fatally out of contact with his original culture; he can't stand to be in the States – "too venal" – but he will never be legitimately African, either.

Until a few weeks ago Dale was working on the shores of Lake Victoria. He was run out of town – literally in his case: he had to get in his truck and drive as men wielding *rungus* (a kind of club) surrounded him – by the members of the fishermen's association he'd been working with, who had been told by the *mganga* (usually translated as "witchdoctor" but actually a traditional healer) that Dale, or more correctly the policies he represents, was destroying their fish stocks.

Dale is philosophical about his predicament. "It was a matter of time really. All the elders were saying the same thing: the rains have changed. Now each year we do not know if they will come back. They're anxious. The *mgangas* look into the future and refuse to tell anyone what they see there. Then I show up with my graphs and charts and reports. Who are they going to blame?"

"But you're all saying the same thing: that the climate is changing, and there will not be enough food."

"Bingo." Dale reaches for his Tusker, which has sweated a pool of condensation around its base. "It's a narrative that's easier to swallow if you are told that it's someone else's fault, that it's coming from somewhere else. I made a promise to tell people the truth. I told them that climate change is in reality not an event but a process, a million adjustments, some of them catastrophic, all over the world. Well, most of them catastrophic."

Dale and I allow our gazes to drift to the jade waters of the shallows in front of the bar. He shakes his head; a refusal, a denial. "This place is so beautiful it hurts."

I agree, thinking of the lacquer of a full moon on the night ocean, the secretive garrison of palms at the end of our sandy lane, the sense of all human intelligence being pitted against the lavish cursive mouth of the beach and what we know is beyond: a distant rotating world of sirens and mulish parks and ordinary urban sloth. All that is unimaginable on our beach and the horizon-awed skies that are its companion, cancelled in the shock of its grinding beauty.

*

The first thing I saw of the man who has become my partner was his architectural drawings for a forest conservation centre he had designed and I was asked to write about, in order to convince people to give money to build it.

The precision of his draftsmanship caught my attention. I had lived on the coast for two months by that point, undertaking lonely missions to buy flour for the conservation organisation where I worked, riding pillion on the back of countless *picky-pickys* – motorcycle taxis. I was on the lookout for a friend who was also of this place, who could be my guide and informant.

He is retired; his ramshackle beach house is bordered by the show homes of the seriously rich. "I have three spare rooms and no one to talk to, apart from Chui," he said. "Why don't you come and stay for a bit?" Chui turned out to be his cat: a rosette-spotted, suspicious creature. I can see how he got his name, which means leopard in Swahili.

In the beach house we have languorous breakfasts under the mbambakofi tree. Our days are tide-tabled. I have downloaded these on my phone: high, low, high, low. Low tide is good for running but bad for swimming. In the afternoons he works on his sculptures and I swim in the ocean. Blue-spotted rays explode from the sandbed beneath me. Swollen seaweed proteas float past on the current. The snout of a black-tipped reef shark heaves into view, then noses away. I get stung by stray tentacles of Portuguese men-of-war which I never see in the ocean itself, only as a hem of blue bubbles on the beach.

On my way back to the house from my run I encounter Mukenka, our *askari*, or night watchman. He has come to the coast only recently. At 5.30 p.m. he arrives wearing Maasai sandals made from discarded car tyres, then changes his shoes to trainers worn with socks, a defence against the puff adders that he might bump into in the night in Maasailand and which would almost certainly kill him, but which are absent on this hot littoral.

We stand side by side and look out to the ocean. He had never seen the sea before coming to work here. In his eyes is a jubilant, terrified expression. "Each day I tell myself, this is real. But the truth is I do not believe it."

"Why did you come here?" I ask.

"There has been a drought in my country" – he refers to Maasailand as a separate polity, even though it is part of Kenya. "Our cattle died, then the goats. My brothers became herdsmen in Tanzania. I came here."

Every night at 7 p.m., just as darkness is falling, the power is cut. We hear a rumour about a ship the government has leased from China to provide wattage for the coast suddenly pulling up its cables and making for Shanghai because the government has neglected to pay its bills. It's quite possible Chui remains oblivious to the niceties of national grid infrastructure in Africa and thinks the chaos is our fault. He gives us a look of disgust (cats are good at these) as the lights stutter, then vanish.

We sit on the sofa and talk, head torches clamped on our foreheads, like despondent miners. I tell him I have begun to think of my life as a complete trajectory, one that I am more than halfway through. Now that my youth is definitively over, I have to mount an effort to project myself into the future, flung there by a mythological structure of subtraction. During my walks along our beach I delete from my personal imaginary of the future the White-browed coucal, the polar ice caps, the tropical lowland forest, then mentally photoshop Cancún-type hotels along the sands.

I was born fifty years ago in a remote corner of eastern Canada and spent my childhood in a seemingly endless winter punctuated by explosive summers. Winters were cold – often minus 30, minus 35 Celsius – and we were surrounded by lynx, wolves, black bears, ptarmigan, rabbits and foxes which adopted white morphs for the winter. Snow was our enemy, a force to be carved through and discarded in order to survive. Most winters after the snow ploughs went by on the highway the snowbanks on either side were as high as the roof of our house.

In my adult life I have done my best to shake off winter, living between the milky climate of the British Isles and the tropics. I am still exploring a lifelong affinity with the tropical zones, despite (or perhaps because of) my boreal origins. What attracts me is the physical ease, the sense of density and interconnections brewed by constant warmth. There is squalor, too, and inequality, but at least no one is going to freeze to death. I still equate cold with deprivation. Given that I grew up poor and living in a trailer on a rust-belt periphery of North America, it seems entirely unlikely that I would end up in a house with a pineapple-shaped swimming pool listening to bushbabies scream in the neem trees. I tell him I feel I have been living several lives at once, in parallel time, or, alternatively, that I have been alive for five hundred years. What my origins and present situation have in common is that they are both perched on the rims of oceans – good places to listen to the beating heart of the planet.

As we talk the sea grinds its gears distantly, a constant backing track, soothing but also somehow exhausting. I wonder if I should tell him what I know about the ocean that claws at his beach only a hundred metres from where we sit now. The Thwaites Glacier in Antarctica has begun what is most likely an unarrestable declination. Currently its melt contributes about 4 per cent of global sea rise, but over the coming decades global sea levels may rise several metres, just because of this one glacier. The oceans really are a planetary ecosystem: an input in one part of the globe will affect every coast. Miami Beach is certain to be under water by 2100. Most houses that will be consumed by the sea in Florida are further from the tideline than the house in which we now sit.

As for the tropics, 40 per cent of humanity lives in the cummerbund that encircles the planet between 23.27 degrees north (the tropic of Cancer) and 23 degrees south (the tropic of Capricorn). The tropics claim most of the African continent, and a good chunk of South America. Southeast Asia and India are almost entirely situated in them. Maps of the climatic zones of the earth often show this band in crimson. Red is of course the colour for heat, although the tropics are definitively green in satellite imagery, and their forest cover is typically referred to as our planet's lungs.

Along with the polar regions, tropical ecosystems are particularly sensitive to climate change. It is thought that a one-degree rise in average global temperature will cause them to release two billion more tonnes of carbon than they did in the 1970s and 1980s, globally. Increased carbon means increased temperatures in a zone that already suffers epic heatwaves and droughts. On a sheer numbers level, studies show that climate change will affect animals, ecosystems and human beings in the tropics more than in other regions.

Then there is the effect of heat on humans. The human body maintains a core temperature of about 37 degrees, higher than the usual ambient temperature. The body needs to dissipate heat effectively; after prolonged exposure to temperatures of 35 degrees this becomes difficult and hyperthermia, or heatstroke, can result. Above 48 degrees, cellular material in the human body begins to thicken, like the albumen in the white of a warming egg. I don't know where I learned this fact – I think it was when I worked in the Brazilian Amazon – but I thought: How interesting, we boil like eggs. Worst-case climate-modelling forecasts for the tropical regions show a rise of between 7 and 12 degrees, taking the zone on earth that is home to almost half of humanity well above the threshold of survivability. A lot of hard-boiled eggs, in other words.

It's mid-September. In two days' time I will be back in London. I run into Dale on the beach. He tells me he sends himself on forced marches up and down its ten-kilometre-long sands each day, "spy missions" he calls them. He squints at me from under a broad white sun hat. "I'm supposed to be recovering from trauma but there's so much skullduggery going on here." I'm so thrilled to hear the word – *skullduggery* – I don't reply.

"Right under KWS's noses," he goes on, referring to the national wildlife body, the Kenya Wildlife Service. "They just sit on their asses and do squat."

"But this is an officially protected environment," I say. "There are two national bodies and three conservation organisations – well, four, depending on how you count them."

His eyes narrow. "That's all very well on paper."

What he means is that in Kenya the laws and national parks with their signs featuring turtles and their smartly outfitted personnel may exist, but the rule of law is weak. Often officials are paid to look the other way.

I tell him I am leaving soon. "What will you do next?" I ask.

"I've got a contract down in Malawi to work on sustainable agriculture in wildlife areas."

"Will you ever go back?" I am well aware this is the wrong question, always, to ask long-term expats, but I am addicted to asking it because their answers are so revealing: of the process of acculturation, identity, of what we have lost in "the West". Europeans and North Americans who have lived in Africa for decades are efficient barometers of what plagues our hyper-controlled, overconfident societies.

"Back where?" Dale replies. "History will be made in Africa, in the twenty-first century. America has fallen on its sword, in electing Donald Trump." He gives me a vague, troubled smile. "There is no 'back', only forward."

The next morning I go running in the smoky dawn. No more tropics television skies for me. By the time darkness falls I will be in Nairobi accepting the breezy smiles of the British Airways crew, and by the morning I will be back in a London tilting towards winter.

Sleepy women hurriedly tying *khangas* around their torsos are awake, as are the village dogs with their razor-clam ribcages. Klaas's cuckoo sings his plangent song. At the end of the road where the creek begins a fisherman is coming back from the beach after an illegal night-time raid on the ocean. He wears a wetsuit half peeled from his body and carries a spear and an octopus in a blue bucket. Without considering what I am about to do I approach the man and persuade him to sell me the octopus and the bucket for five hundred shillings.

The octopus is a gelatinous tangle. In the nest of limbs I can pick out a head, moist and smooth as a newborn baby's crown. The tentacles make forays to the lip of the bucket, seizing it delicately, before falling back. I remember reading that octopuses have three hearts and little control over their arms, which are operated by a trio of separate nervous systems.

I run with the octopus sloshing in the bucket to the nearest beach. The morning sky is dark with storm clouds. I leave my trainers on the sand. I have no goggles with me and I have to do an awkward sidestroke into the choppy waves with my stronger arm. The octopus has perked up. His head appears above the rim. One of his two eyes fixes on me. He has an eyelid and a knowing dark iris.

"Hold your horses," I say, then laugh, and then remember that laughing when you are in water over your head and trying to swim with an octopus in a bucket is not a good idea. I inhale water and for a second panic.

The octopus's arms billow onto the surface of the water. His head has flattened, like a collapsed soufflé. He floats for a moment, bobbing in the waves. Then he dissolves into the ocean, sliding down towards a rock where he can hide until the next spear fisherman arrives. I tread water for a while until it starts to rain, and I can't see him any more.

POETRY

EMILY HINSHELWOOD
RONAN FITZGERALD
LAWRENCE ILLSLEY

"AMENDMENTS TO UK GOVERNMENT POLICY ON BIODIVERSITY"

– IN THE LIGHT OF THE LATEST CLIMATE RESEARCH

EMILY HINSHELWOOD

Executive Summary
So, we lose the cuckoo wasp
which smells of dianthus.
Will anybody really notice?

Amendment 1: Extinction – latest records
As each species goes extinct
remove the relevant page from the wildlife book.

We lose the lacewing, whose eggs float on filaments.
The harlequin, the whirligig. The silver-washed fritillary,
the *Bombus distinguendis*: more commonly known as
the Great Yellow Bumblebee.
We lose warblers and babblers and wombats and vangas
red flying squirrels, pink armadillos
dragons and dromedaries and ring-tailed rock wallabies
golden-crowned
royal-crested, satin-breasted
sweet-lipped, fire-bellied
whistling, wild
wandering
weedy, ruddy
legless, flightless
stinky, snapping
screaming
slit-faced, funnel-eared
bottle-nosed, big-headed
lump-sucking, parasitic ...

Amendment 2: New Diversity Definition
The Wealth of any particular society
is measured by the diversity of items on the menu.

Amendment 3: Hosting Immigrants – with overseas report from our chief executive
New figures show that 44% of immigrants to the UK have agreed to be genetically modified.
This has substantially reduced the amount of food required.

On a small archipelago, Miss Abi chalks up a long-division sum
on the blackboard. Children sit cross-legged on the floor.
She's carrying the figure 4 past the decimal point, when water
laps under the door. This has happened before.
"Move," she says, "move away from the door."
But by midday, the blackboard is floating
children are rescued in dugout boats
with goats and sacks of grain and Miss Abi is shouting
"It's just a freak wave"
but there's whooping and rippling
and gulping and gliding
and dunking and splashing.
The sea has gone above the water mark –
and it's dragging and tossing and rolling
and tearing with loggerhead turtles
and elephant sharks.

Up in the sky we're stuck in air traffic
licking the last salty peanuts from the packet.
The steward hands out tiny bottles of wine
and individually wrapped plastic knives.

Amendment 4: Sea Level Rise
The length of your life is in direct proportion
to how tall your house is.

And at this stage, our life is like a yacht
and when the yacht begins to rock and strain
above the waves, it's like an ice skate
and when the skate begins to lose control ...

Amendment 5: Biosecurity
The security company G4S, which won the multi-billion-pound
contract to guard the links in the food chain, has revealed that
the last queen bee on earth has gone missing. The army has been
drafted in to undertake a plant-to-plant search.

Amendment 6: Toxic Algae Warning
"Do not, I repeat, do not go back into the water,"
says government phycologist Mr George.

Phycology, he corrects the BBC reporter,
is not the study of phucking
though when he chose his course
this is actually what he thought it was.

Amendment 7: Food Chain Breakdown
A controversial court case in Merthyr Tydfil has set a precedent
for dealing with food chain issues.

It is now law that rich people are entitled to eat poor people.

... and when the ice skate begins to lose control, it's like a flame
    and if the flame takes hold
    it tears through trees like a herd of beasts
    and when the herd has trampled
    all the living plants, it's like a desert breeze.

Amendment 8: UK Home Office Practical Tips
You can attach an umbrella to your head
with wire, string and Sellotape but not Blu Tack.

Amendment 9: Semantics
Endangered species that are not of a red colour will henceforth
be removed from the Red List.

This cuts the number of endangered species by approximately 98%.

Kisi, from Bodo,
sprinkles OMO detergent on a freshly caught fish.
Scrapes black oil from its scales until it's not too hard to eat.
She steps across pipes
where her brother was burnt to bits
in a "minor" leak.

Amendment 10: What Help Can We Expect From Outside?
God has all but given up.
He's rarely seen outside these days.
He buys his diesel from the old lady
in the market who pushes her fifty-litre barrel
up from the port at Swansea and sells it by the jugload.

But the angels start a new life.
One skims her halo like a Frisbee.
"Wherever it lands" – she races after it – "I'll keep planting trees."
"I'll open springs," she adds, "and drink till the water runs clear.
I'll crack out buds –
and release the pollen from forget-me-nots
celandines
anemones
betonies
bryonies
daisies
poppies."

And when the warning's heard, it's like the birth of a song, like morning:
whistling
wild
sweet-lipped, fire-bellied
royal-crested, satin-breasted
golden-crowned
dawn.

THE GIRL IN THE ORANGE DRESS

RONAN FITZGERALD

A found poem made from headlines in the Guardian's *"Experience" section: https://www.theguardian.com/lifeandstyle/ series/experience*

Born without a tongue,
Born with no ears,
Blind.
I lived in the dark,
Alone.
The quietest place on earth.

Like a deaf opera singer,
I dreamed a symphony, then composed it.
I dreamed the song of my lover's kiss.
Stung, swept, impaled by my own sculpture,
I finally heard the sound.

I fell in love,
I fell down an escalator,
off a viaduct,
off a mountain,
off a cliff,
I was swept away by a flood.
I had Alice in Wonderland syndrome,
my love a sweet macropsia.
I said yes to marriage
the first time we met.

Fatherhood was like
growing wild mushrooms
in a death camp,
like working as a barman
in Antarctica,
like being a Japanese prisoner of war.
I lost the power of language,

I signed away my life.
For years we lived in a coma,
buried alive,
then I read about her affair in her diary.

I didn't leave the house for a decade,
My hair fell out in a weekend,
I couldn't recognise my own face.
A man being strangled,
I talked only with my eyes.

Now, I live with someone I've lost.
A machine,
locked in her own body, barely alive.
And I too have an artificial heart,
I too am unfaithful.
A sex-somniac, hunting at night,
a mountain lion, a great white.

I am a sperm donor for my friends.
I sleep with Big Bird, a Jedi,
a one-legged tap dancer, a secret nude model.
I sleep with the man who saved me from drowning,
I sleep with wolves.

I have a worm in my brain.
I have a cockroach in my ear.
I was bitten by a rattlesnake.

10 years, 11 years, 29, 37,
I can't stop stealing
from the past.
In my head it's 1975,
I fell in love at the supermarket checkout.

BOOM

LAWRENCE ILLSLEY

A pink shotgun cartridge lands on the grass.
Five unbagged beer bottles, moraines marooned,
lie like frost-shattered bones, erratic glass.
Polyethylene strands, red, white and blue,

untressed like hair, spill over the corrie,
the delta of a misfit stream. The sun
burns a spyhole in a derelict sky.
The boy necks a bottle, reloads his gun

and shoots. Sound fills the combe, a glacial
boom. Oil tubs bob on the sinusoidal
surface of the black tarn. From a tree branch
a hung shoe swings like a fresh-popped eyeball.

He exhales. Silence. Two beats, a minim.
Behind him the Anthropocene rolls in.

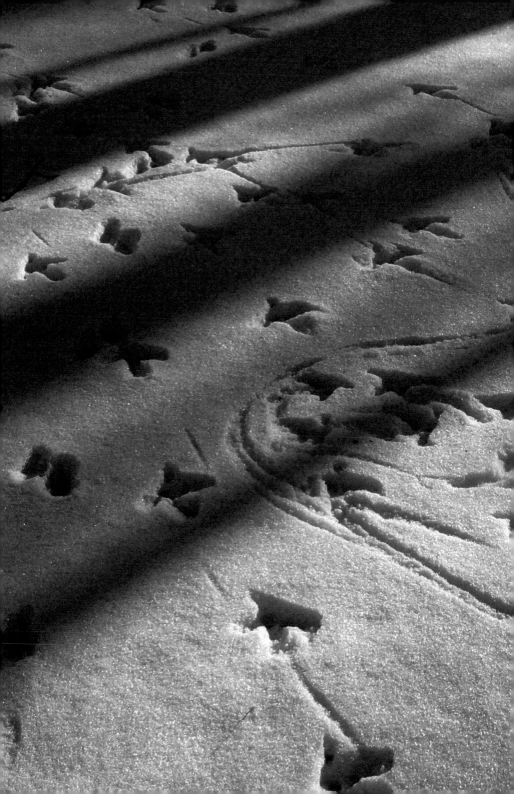

FICTION

GOLD

LORRAINE WILSON

The snow falls slantwise onto ground that has not yet had a chance to freeze. She wears neither coat nor hat, but goes out into the garden bearing gifts of sunflower hearts and suet balls and bruised apples. Cluster-flakes are melting into her hair but the air is bitter rather than sharp. A single blackbird in the hedge watches her darkly, his beak a tiny flame against the dormant branches.

She throws him apples and he cants his head but does not move. Once the feeders are replenished and the lawn scattered with riches, she retreats inside, wet-headed, to watch from the window as the blackbird returns. He long-hops as if suspended from above, neither flying nor falling, and she would watch him longer but the day's clockwork summons her to lunch boxes, bags and coats and a dozen small errands. The car again, the office, emails and meetings, yet again the colleague whose eyes linger where they should not, and then, so many things half done, it is school and shop and home carrying excitement like a storm in the car because the snow that faltered before is back again, turning the tops of puddles viscous and threatening the road's valiant salt. It will be dark by the time her husband drives home.

Be careful, she texts, but he is in meetings and does not reply.

As she cooks, the light beyond her window shifts from grey day to sooty night, the snow settling so the ground is lighter than the sky, the world inverted. If she leans forward she can see snowflakes circling the streetlights like moths and she imagines some strange white bat swooping out of the dark to feast.

The snow waits three inches deep by morning, more where the wind gathered furbelows against fences, less in the shadows beneath the hedge and the juniper which has cloaked itself sumptuously, guarding the earth like a hawk.

There is food in the feeders, but she scatters more on top of the snow. A robin comes today, brazen, and two blackbirds in the sycamore watching each other instead of her. Once she is inside a flock falls into the tree alongside them, tiny against the turbid clouds, fragments of gold and red and freedom. They always leave her a little breathless, a little blessed, these goldfinches tumbling down into her garden to feed, and for a moment she ignores the children shrieking.

Today she has no meetings and leaves the office on time for once, unrushed. Her husband is away tonight, and the evening promises an obstacle course of piano lessons, judo, a snatched supper, bedtime, and then an eventual peace. The roads grow nasty, gritty slush sliding beneath the tyres so that her knuckles whiten and she regrets not staying home.

The newspapers talk of deep freezes and climate change, they murmur or clamour or debate according to the dictates of their owners. This, though, is all she knows: that the snow is different now, a white painting of white chaos, unsentient but strangely alive. The children are ecstatic, snow-figures gathering in the park, erratically dressed, and she is torn between deadlines and the lure of their febrile excitement, the child inside her wanting to break free.

By morning there is a foot of it, the landscape of the garden gentled, topography smoothed and every bare branch an artwork so that to walk in it is sacrilege, even as more falls to erase her passage, her presence. Her blood burrows deep into her body, chasing summer, her hands stinging as she holds the feeders, and her breath is a sea fog around her head, crystallising in the air. The food from yesterday is gone, but whether eaten or buried she cannot say, and above her head she can hear the goldfinches twitter-calling, waiting for her offerings, her absence. Tilting her head back, she has to blink snowflakes out of her eyes to catch glimpses of the flock silhouetted against the falling sky; she cannot see their colours, only their movement. Twenty of them, perhaps thirty, and she wants to stay there, turning white and numb until they forget her and come down. She wants to see the gold in their wings and the scarlet on their faces, the way they scold and enjoin and chase as if they are bound together with a webwork of strings.

But the kids come through the back door, shouting, "School's closed, Mum! School's closed!" waving her phone gleefully as above her the flock wheels away, snow effacing them as if they had never been real but were only a fabrication, joy made miniature and numerous and loud. So instead of work, she has clamorous children, a bundled walk to the park where other mothers huddle penguin-like as the children hurl themselves into the weather like fireworks. The snow falls and the kids play until their hands hurt to unfold and ice has balled itself beneath their clothes, their cheeks red as roses and how wonderful a thing to be gifted a day like this, she thinks. But it is too cold to linger now; the snow falls and the thermometer falls too, lower and still lower, and tonight will be terrible, she thinks, their radiators will press against the winter beyond the walls. But what a miraculous, lucky thing, to have walls and radiators and beds heavy with all the duvets that they own.

They eat soup so hot it scalds their mouths, and her husband comes home early, the roads closing around them as if the landscape is a stopped heart, the roads its dying vessels.

The snow falls and sometime in the night, it stops.

In the morning she goes out again, stamping beneath the feeder until it is a packed white arena marred by twiglets and sand from the soles of her boots. She can almost hear her husband complaining about the damage she is doing to the grass beneath, but with the feeders empty and the garden full of black eyes watching, she doesn't care.

One of the children joins her but he wears no coat and the air is so cold she can feel frost fractals in her lungs, so that it hurts to breathe, and when will they develop common sense, she asks herself half-heartedly, sending him back inside. She holds a guilty truth, that she is happier out here alone with her buried garden and the waiting birds. A robin comes to her feet, the great darkness of his eyes on her as he pecks at suet. How hungry he must be, to have balanced her threat and his hunger and come so close. How hungry and how brave, fluffing himself spherical, misleadingly round and desperately combating the cold.

Today, because her husband is inside and no one will be going anywhere, she doesn't return to the house but pours warm water into a basin then brushes clear the bench and sits, her face numb and the tips of her fingers burning inside her gloves. The sky is such a thin blue that she thinks its facets might cut her like glass if she only raised her hand.

First come the blackbirds, seven, eight of them, coffee browns and coal, spacing themselves in precarious harmony because food matters more today than feuds and territories, food to become warmth, to become tomorrows.

And now the goldfinches. She has been waiting for them. The volume of their calls rises; but for her presence? Or the hope in the hearts of sunflowers, summer given back to them in seeds? She smiles a little, and tries to count although their restlessness makes it hard. Thirty-five? Thirty-eight? Their tiny size against the wide, white wilderscape is phenomenal to her; in the simple fact of their existence, she can read the whole spectrum of her dreams.

They find the water too, in twos and threes on the blue rim, dipping the very tips of their beaks delicately to drink, and she watches them until she can no longer feel her legs, until she has stopped shivering and her eyes are stiff in their sockets in a way she had not known possible.

Then her husband opens a window, calling out to her, and anger rises as all the birds flush from their food. Because how dare he put her welfare above that of such tiny wonders, who have no warm mug of tea to thaw them, who must wait out the coming night with only their feathers and her food?

She sighs and her body creaks as she straightens, as if shedding a layer of ice, as if calving herself from the glacier of the air.

She puts more food out after lunch, and melts the ice in the birdbath with steaming water from the kettle. It will freeze within minutes, but she hopes they will come down before it does, before the short day surrenders and the snow returns. Its clouds are already on the horizon, and it unsettles her, how much she fears for the birds. As if this dense and terrible cold is more than just weather now, as if it is something pivotal, and this is a thought that comes again as the day dies and the ice blue of the sky is erased once more. That there are points of gold in our lives, and if we do not care then we will lose them; if they become rare then we are lost.

*

The snow falls so heavily in the night that she is woken by the sound of it slipping over tiles and down the windows. Yet in the morning there is angled sunlight so sharp it coruscates the air, casting rainbows.

Her family are still in bed when she steps into this fierce light. Coming to the lawn, she thinks the patches of colour beneath a veil of snow are yesterday's food, unfinished.

But then she sees that they are not.

Kneeling beneath the feeder, gasping denial and heartbreak, No, she begs, snow melting against her knees as she reaches out, and No, because there is gold in the snow and scarlet. They were never meant to be so still, so banished from their skies. Their eyelids are pale as the snow around them. The tears on her lashes become ice. Shedding her gloves impatiently because she cannot bear to touch the birds through her own protections. It would be too cruel.

She gathers them into her hands, not counting but weighing, cradling their tiny bodies against her. How can beauty weigh so little? How can they possibly be so still when yesterday they argued and danced and sang?

The snow falls and she keens without words, curled over them as if she can save them, as if she can make a shield of her own body and undo the cruel night. She carries them to the hedge and lays them gently, one by one, into a blanket of last year's leaves. Their bodies are stiff but their feathers are softer than the snow on her hands. Her face is mazed with frozen tears, her ribs aching because how can this be fair, that they should die and she can walk back into the warm?

Her husband hands her tea at the door, frowning at her tears, and she does not try to explain because she has left her heart out in the garden, out in the snow.

THE COSMOPOLITAN

FICTION

THE MIRAGE
CASINO & RESORT

BEATLES
LOVE
CIRQUE DU SOLEIL.
BRIGHTER. BOLDER. BIGGER.

THE VOICE OF ENTERTAINMENT
TERRY FATOR

THIS PLACE IS NO VEGAS

K. M. ELKES

Tommy's at poker night getting thrashed again. He's had nothing but hand after hand of utter dross until these two kings. Now the feels are on him, the same as when his dead father shows himself with a soft thud in an empty next-door room or through a sudden swell of heat on night-time roads that makes Tommy wind down the window of his van. It is a sign to concentrate. Take his opportunity. Get a win.

They've been doing poker night for years, Tommy and Dexter and Joe. Wednesdays, eight on the dot, a decent beer on tap and the blessed click of the chips. Always round at Dexter's because he's got a fine table and buys a fresh deck of cards every few months, the show-off prick.

There was a fourth. Dexter's twin, Max, dead at fifty-four, his heart emptied of beats. And yet he did everything right: ran half marathons for the hospice, got the finger up the bum at fifty, cut the fat off his bacon. All so he could die face down on the bathroom floor with his trousers round his ankles. Toilet roll everywhere, as though he'd been scrabbling at it like a kitten. As if it would do anything but unravel. They still set out a chair at the table for Max, though they've backed off pulling a pint for him each week.

"Truth is, my brother was a lightweight. A thimble drunk," said Dexter.

"Harsh on a dead man," said Tommy.

"But fair," said Joe.

Tommy looks at his cards again, resists the urge to rub at the mole on his chin. It's a telltale sign with Joe and Dexter watching, alert as gulls round a chippie. Joe is next up to bet. He stares at his cards for a while then puts them face down on the table, walks to the door and opens it to the night. Joe's got irritable bowel and an arse like an abattoir, so they've worked out a system. But this is a clear stalling tactic to unnerve Tommy, as though Joe's some Texas Hold'em pro in a big tournament.

They have talked, over the years, about a Las Vegas trip. About setting up an account between them to save a bit of cash each month, enough to buy flights and have some fun money. Joe said they have slot machines right there at the airport, so you can play while you wait for the luggage carousel to spit out your bags.

Tommy has it all lined up in his head. They would walk out of McCarran International and straight outside Departures would be a white '59 Cadillac convertible, with the huge fins and the red leather seats. They would drive slow-slow up Las Vegas Boulevard, getting the full 360, a new Rat Pack come to town, and inspect the landmarks, the shiny blackness of the Luxor pyramid, the Fountains of Bellagio going off like fireworks while music blared, then over Flamingo Road to Caesar's Palace and the Mirage and up past the polished copper of the Wynn Hotel bouncing light everywhere, all the way to the Stratosphere Tower, before heaving a U-turn and driving right back down again.

A suite in the Venetian, that's what the lads reckon. Like Venice but in Vegas, so it kills two birds with one stone, according to Dexter. A ridiculous notion, of course – how is a canal in the desert like the bloody Venice waterways? In truth, Tommy would prefer some vintage motel, a bit rough round the edges maybe, but old school, more authentic. Besides, wouldn't they be out and about most of the time, only popping back for a quick wash and brush-up and a few hours' kip? Wasn't that the point – you spent your time at the tables or in the lounges listening to the crooners or just wandering, sucking it down into your lungs, tasting the place in your mouth. The smell of money on your fingers.

In the casino all he wants is one good hour with a slick dealer and a friendly crowd. Cheers and groans from the roulette tables and the mad jangle of the slot machines in the background. Those lasses in the slinky numbers bringing free drinks and people gathered behind his table, three or four deep, to watch him take a big win on the turn of a card (he always imagines the king of spades), enough to make the crowd clap and whoop and for Tommy to toss the dealer a chip or two. And then off to the little window in the wall to collect his cash so, for once, his wallet would be fat against his arse.

"Are you going to blow-dry that patio all night or play cards, Joseph?" Dexter asks.

You never see Dexter ruffled. Can never tell what he's thinking. Would be a dab hand at poker if he could be bothered to learn the rules. But Dexter doesn't worry too much about it, because he's had the success, relatively speaking. Works indoors and lives on the new estate. Commutes, for God's sake. You have to know the combination to unlock old Dexter – mostly single malts and a few croaked lines of *The Fields of Athenry* because his father was Irish. Only when pissed-up and wet-eyed will Dexter confess that the reason there is a strip of wild, unmown grass at the bottom of his garden is because he sees visions of himself and Max down there as little kids, playing among the dandelion clocks and creeping buttercups, not quite split, so he says, because they are still joined at their very fingertips.

Joe makes his way back to the table. Pushes his little tower of plastic chips to the middle with an exaggerated flourish. He's "all in".

"Let's have it then," he says.

Tommy looks at his cards once more, as if somehow they might have changed into something even better. Still, it is a pair of kings. Not good, not bad, but all he has got.

"Game on then," says Dexter and goes all in with his own pile of chips.

Tommy shakes his head, looks at them both. So bloody typical. His one chance all night and now this. He doesn't have enough left to match them. The bet's moved on and they've sidelined him. He sits for a moment, then bends and unlaces his shoes, puts them on the table, socks tucked inside. He folds his coat and places it next to the shoes.

"I call," he says.

"What's this business?" says Joe.

"That's bending the rules, T," says Dexter.

"These shoes are shop-bought," says Tommy. "And the coat. Not from the market. They're worth something."

"So what? None of us is exactly staking fortunes here. This fashion-parade bullshit's too much."

"Call it a gesture or whatever the fuck you like. Are we playing to win or not?" asks Tommy.

"This," says Dexter, removing his glasses and pinching the bridge of his nose, "is why I say we play for coins."

"I'll ask again. Are we playing to win or not?"

Joe winks and says: "I'll take them," then lays down two aces.

The old dread slides over Tommy. The feels fade and he has to regroup.

"All right, smug lad. Wait for the turn card," he says.

Dexter reaches for the stack, slides off the top card. A king is turned. It's still on!

"Now then," says Tommy. "Now then."

They each take a sup then lean in, spotlit by the bulb Dexter has suspended from the ceiling, ready for the finale. Dexter licks his finger and thumb then turns the last card, the river. It's another ace. Joe whistles, reaches out and rakes in the pot. Tommy leans back, slow-punctured.

"That's rubbing it in. I mean, dear God, the chances of that on the river card," he says.

"More like shit-creek card," says Joe. "And you without a paddle."

He pushes the coat and shoes across the table.

"No! No fucking way. You take them," says Tommy.

"Give over. Your feet are like boats, man."

"Take them!"

Dexter pipes up: "Tommy, we're not in the Wild West here. Ease up."

"He won, so he'll take them."

Joe sighs then pulls the shoes and coat from the table.

"Good. Then I'll see you boys soon," says Tommy and fixes on his best poker face as he leaves, feet slapping and sucking on the cold floor of Dexter's lean-to.

Outside, a moon is up and the air still warm enough not to need the coat he has lost. The streets smell of dust and there is heat, he is sure of it, left in the pavement under his bare soles.

He doesn't know which way to go, except that he cannot go home, not yet. Adele will be awake, wrapped in her old grey dressing gown, sitting on the bed not in it, because even after all these years she likes to get under the covers at the same time. If she sees him barefoot and coatless it will be "Tommy this" and "Tommy that" and the full hose-down about how him and the boys are just old idiots keeping off the boredom playing silly card games. Worse still, when he gets into bed, she will put her arms around him and rest her head on his chest. She will ask him if he is all right and what, just what, should she do with him. These are questions he cannot answer.

Sometimes, when Adele is out, he unhooks her dressing gown from the back of the door and puts his face in it. The scent reminds him of when they were young and frantic with life. Frantic for a place of their own and frantic to fuck and frantic about danger when the kids were little. Back then he watched her sleep, filled with a mix of desire and a strange fear that she would not wake up. Now he watches for comfort, the bulk of her under the covers rounded as a hill, the dog spooned into her.

If he can avoid a scene with Adele tonight, Joe will call round in the morning. He knows that much. There will be some awkward banter about the weather or the garden or the car. Joe will say something funny enough to make them both laugh and then he will give the shoes and coat back. He will make an excuse to go and when he does, he will leave the gate wide open, just for a laugh. Tommy will put the coat and shoes in the cramped, dark cupboard under the stairs. He will stay in there for a while.

Tommy reaches the end of Dexter's street and crosses, wary of dog shit and glass under his toes. He turns into the park and walks on, past the playground, where the swings and slide and see-saw are empty and still in the moonlight. There are good memories in this place. His eldest, Grace, as a toddler, giggling her way down the slide and him after her, the big monster man on the chase, only not sliding but getting his fat arse wedged against the sides and having to hump his way down. Grace laughed like he was the funniest thing ever. There was a softness, a golden tinge, to the light that afternoon, and he'd said to Adele, Let's not go just yet. They stayed until dusk, until Grace was overtired and hungry and bored of their games.

Beyond the playground are the lights of the new estate. He can hear the thump-thump-thump of bass speakers in some kid's car slinking round the cul-de-sacs and looping roads. He listens as it grows and fades and the night stills again. He can hear the lads in his head: "Don't be starting your 'when this was all fields' shit. Nobody needs the details of your happy place, Tommy."

"My happy place is anywhere you pair aren't," Tommy says out loud. These words, old familiar banter, are fixed in his head. They are like a trusted tool, polished and weighted just right.

Besides, it really was all fields, once. As boys they built a den into the embankment of the old railway line, deep into a thicket of ash saplings. They skipped school to hide there, lining the floor with offcuts of old carpet that smelled of chemical toilets. Joe brought the ripped-out pages of porn mags filched from the newsagent, while Dexter provided a tin of half-smoked cigarette ends, the tips still sweet with his mum's lipstick. Max joined them only after school because goody-two-shoes Max wasn't the sort to feign illness or miss double bloody geography.

Except, of course, *that* time. Tommy had sneaked up one hot June day to scare the life out of whoever was in the den. He crouched close, saw two pairs of shoes and recognised them as Joe's and Max's. In the mouth of the den he could see their bare feet and bare legs, one set of toes rubbing gently against the other, then the legs mixed up together. He crouched there a long time, until a plane went overhead, and he used the noise as cover to leave. He never told a soul. They were his mates and it was their secret to keep.

Tommy finds a track, a channel of earth hard and smooth beneath his bare feet, that takes him diagonally across the park and down the long slope to the boating lake. He heads towards the wooden hut where they sell ice creams and teas and tickets for the sun-bleached pedalos in the water, a plastic flock of swans and flamingos and dragons.

There is a bench by the hut, under the light cast by a single street lamp. If he looks hard enough Tommy could still find his name carved into the bench seat, scored by a compass from his pencil case a million years ago. After the den was flattened, the boating lake was where they came to hang around and smoke and drink from a shared bottle and talk about girls. They grew into men in this spot, and not so many years later, brought their own kids down. Adele had insisted they visit the park and boating lake every Saturday in summer. The kids liked the routine, apparently. They would all sit on this very bench, licking ice-cream cones, looking up at the old prefabs on the hill. It was mostly old people who lived up there and on Saturdays they all put their sheets and towels out on the lines. Squint and the place looked like a sailing ship on a slipway, ready to slide down into the little boating lake and land with a splash.

Tommy wipes his hand over his face. All these memories. They billow through his mind constantly these days. He can't escape them anywhere he goes. They are layered across the landscape of the town, like new wallpaper on top of old.

He sits on the bench and contemplates his feet. His ankles give off a volley of clicks when he flexes and rolls them loose in the mornings, while his toes are boxy and the yellow nails even yellower under the street light. Now, after his walk through the park, the soles are mucky with dust and grass and earth and whatever else he has collected. What a sorry state, Adele would say. But no one ever sees my feet, he would reply.

He hears footsteps, then a cough. Out of the shadows by the wooden hut comes a pasty face. A lad only just out of his teens, at a guess, acne about his cheeks and a try-out beard, patchy as weeds, on his chin. Tommy thinks he recognises the face, or at least the features of the father or mother in it. Adele would know straight off. She knows everyone. When the kid spots him, he stops still, like a cat discovered at the butter dish.

"All right then," Tommy says. "Fair tonight, weather-wise."

"You got a light?" the lad asks. He comes closer, looks down at Tommy's bare feet, then withdraws again.

"Never mind an' all," he says.

He wears a T-shirt that shows a cartoon toddler dressed in a onesie, smoking a cigar and holding a machine gun. Underneath is written: *In my defence, I was left unsupervised.* But the cartoon joke doesn't match up with the droop of the lad's shoulders, or the sour look of his face, or the wounded way he walks, like he has broken bones. It's this that makes Tommy check for a lighter he knows he doesn't have.

"I've one somewhere," says Tommy, patting his pockets. "I'm sure I recognise your face. What's your name?"

"Aaron. You probably know my dad. Everyone knows my dad."

"Your dad's name ... Pete?"

"Pat."

"That's the bloke."

Tommy knows Pat. Knows of him, the reputation, at least. There are plenty enough stringy kids in town who call Pat Dad.

"So, what brings you out here tonight, son of Pat?"

"It doesn't matter," the lad says. He has found a lighter in a pocket and turns back the way he came.

"You got a spare one of them, Aaron?" asks Tommy.

The young man hesitates, then offers the packet and the lighter. Tommy doesn't know why – he'd rather be alone – but he raps the bench seat next to him with his knuckles.

"Take a pew, Aaron. You look like you could do with company. Let the joy of mine wash over you," he says.

The kid sits. The cigarette tastes harsh. The smoke is glasspaper on Tommy's throat. It's the first one he's touched since Max went. He watches his new companion out of the corner of his eye. Aaron stares straight ahead at the dark water of the lake while the cigarette he holds smoulders to a long finger of ash, until he pinches it out in a sudden blaze of sparks and flicks the remains into the bushes. He runs chewed nails through his hair. He rubs the heel of his hand into his eyes. He sighs and stares and is silent. This one, thinks Tommy, would be no good at poker.

"Are you going to let me get a word in edgeways?" asks Tommy.

The kid shrugs, then asks: "Why aren't you wearing shoes?"

"Tell me why you're out here and I might tell you the story in return."

With only a little more cajoling Aaron shows his hand. He has a baby son and lives with his girlfriend, whose name is Eliza, in one of the prefabs on the hill. The baby is called Callum and hardly sleeps because of eczema. Callum has been on life support more than once for his lungs. Aaron and Eliza have split twice already. Aaron is on zero-hours contracts and zero-hours sleep.

Tommy shakes his head. "Have you thought about stand-up comedy with that routine?"

"Fine. I'll be off then," says Aaron.

"Sit down! I don't mean any harm. I know what it's like with a young family. I used to come down here myself when it all got a bit much, meet up with a mate of mine, Max. The thing you need to know is this lake is only a few feet deep, just chest high, even in the middle. But in the dark, you can pretend it's as big and deep as any ocean. And in summertime, the water's so shallow it keeps warm. They were good times. Kept us afloat, so to speak."

The last time, many years ago now, a good summer was nearly done. He can picture it, the water so still it shone like glass under the moon. Him and Max waded in, splitting light in their wake. They headed for the middle to float on their backs and stare up at the sky and everything seemed right for a while.

"You serious? You used to swim in that pisshole?"

Part of Tommy wants to walk away and leave Aaron to his misery. To do whatever stupidity the lad has come to do. But he can hear himself, the young Tommy, in Aaron's hard tone. And whenever old Tommy thinks of young Tommy, whenever he looks at the pictures of himself in the photo albums, Tommy gets mixed up, feels both jealousy and sorrow at the same time.

"Look, lad, I know this place is no Vegas," he says, "but it's not as bad as you think."

"Vegas? Happens that I've been there. I went over last year."

Tommy doesn't say a word. Can't say a word. Instead he reaches up to worry at the mole on his chin.

"Eliza's dad won this prize-draw thing," Aaron continues. "It was the second prize, not even the first. That was a cruise. That would have been even worse."

"Even worse?" asks Tommy, pinching at the mole as if he could pluck it from his face.

"Yeah. See, the thing with Vegas is you fly over darkness for ever, just desert and fuck all, then the pilot tells you to look out of the window and there it is – lights shining out of nowhere, all oranges and whites and reds. And when you get closer and lower you can see the Strip all lit up, brighter than anything else, these massive towers and casinos just bursting out of the desert. It's amazing."

"I can imagine," says Tommy. "I can."

Aaron is silent for a few moments, as though gathering up a story he is reluctant to tell.

"But that's the best of it. That first night it's all big lights and big tits and big crowds and your head on a swivel. Nobody tells you how Vegas smells – all those hotels and casinos have got their own smell they pump out of the air conditioning. It's mad! The place is dialled up to eleven. But in the daytime ... See, we were staying in this big hotel, swanky like, but next to it was one of those little casinos that must have been built way back, called the Gold Mine or something. The swimming pool was dried out and there were piles of broken chairs in the far end of the car park. And all the staff were dressed in this beige get-up that must have been from the 1980s or something. In the mornings they shipped in old people using school buses. Can you believe it! I knew from that they weren't pumping a special smell into the place, unless it was fuckin' bleach and pine cleaner."

He stops, pulls out the cigarette packet and takes two, passing one to Tommy, lighting them both.

"It's like the sun out there is so hard and bright you can't hide anything," says Aaron. "It's just ... I thought there'd be more to it, you know?"

Tommy feels as though he has seen an ace turned while holding two shit kings. That same dread as earlier, the one he knows too well from his own sleepless nights, not for kids crying, but for a grief he can't even explain. Those three o'clock in the morning times, when there is no light behind the curtains and no sign of dawn. And more often lately, when he has been out walking the dog and stopped on the bridge over the dual carriageway, the smell of steel on his hands, eyes closed and filling himself only with the roar and stink of the traffic.

Aaron looks at him, the same way that Joe and Dexter looked at him earlier, waiting for his move. And when Tommy thinks of this he understands, for the first time, that he has never known, not really, when to bluff and when to fold. That he doesn't even know what's the bluff and what's the truth these days. All he knows is that it's his move. So he stubs out his cigarette, stands and pulls off his top. His belly bounces free from beneath it and rests over the top of his trousers until he removes these too.

"Vegas doesn't interest me," Tommy shouts as he undresses. "Forget Vegas. Fuck Vegas!"

He walks to the concrete lip of the boating lake and stoops for a moment to brush dirt from the bottom of each foot. "So are you coming in or what?"

"Coming in?" Aaron looks towards the lake and grimaces. "To that?"

"Trust me," says Tommy. "Duck piss and lake muck – they should bottle and sell it."

He wades into the lukewarm water and keeps pushing on as it rises to his waist. There is a layer of silt on the bottom and the feel of it under his feet is the same as all those years ago, awful and beautiful at the same time. Silk and slime, Max called it. Tommy stops, squeezes his toes together a few times, then sinks into the water and rolls onto his back.

"You never told me," shouts Aaron. He's come away from the bench to the lake. "You never told me why you had bare feet."

"Come on in then. When we get to the middle I'll tell you it all, the whole sorry tale. Come on. Get in!"

Tommy lays his head back and lets the water fold and gutter around his body. He gazes up to the ripe, white moon. He drifts, and drifts away, and somewhere in that drifting feels himself risen from the water, lifted into the warm air so he can gaze down on himself, suspended in the lake below, surrounded by the flotilla of swans and flamingos and dragons. And as he rises higher still, he sees revealed the whole lake, the park, the new estate, the old town and the fields and woods beyond, until, somewhere in the deepest part of the dark, he sees the bright lights of another place.

NOTES ON CONTRIBUTORS

PICTURE CREDITS

ARHONDIA is a Greek-Irish writer. Growing up in Athens sparked a love for theatre and storytelling. Having moved to Ireland after completing school she studied theatre at the Conservatory of Music and Drama (DIT) in Dublin and storytelling in pubs all across the country. Arhondia completed her MA in creative writing at Birkbeck in 2018, and begins a PhD at King's College London in October 2019. Her short story "Tom Corridan" was published in *The Mechanics' Institute Review* Issue 15.

LOUISA ARMITAGE has been writing short stories for ten years. She has just completed an MA in creative writing at Birkbeck, University of London, where she began to write poetry. She is a new mother and has focused her work around themes including maternity and nature. "Baby" is her first poetry submission to an anthology.

HANNAH AUSTIN is a writer and editor from South Wales. Her fiction and creative non-fiction have appeared in the *Guardian*, *The Moth*, *Mslexia*, *Hippocampus*, *The Real Story*, *Litro Online*, *New Welsh Review* and elsewhere. She was a finalist in the *Aesthetica* Creative Writing Award 2018, the Fish Short Memoir Prize 2019 and the Centre for Women Writers' International Literary Awards 2019. She is currently working on her first book, a hybrid memoir, for which she was awarded an Arts Council England grant earlier this year. Find her online at HannahAustinWriter.com and @HAustinEditor.

ELIZABETH BAINES' stories have appeared in numerous journals and anthologies including *Short Fiction* and Salt's *Best British Short Stories*. Two collections, *Balancing on the Edge of the World* and *Used to Be*, are published by Salt. Salt also published her novel *Too Many Magpies* and reissued her novel *The Birth Machine*, which has been considered a feminist classic. She is a prize-winning playwright for Radio 4 and has performed and produced her own plays for fringe theatre. She was a founder editor with Ailsa Cox of the short-story magazine *metropolitan*. A new novel, *Astral Travel*, will be published by Salt in 2020.

SARAH BARR writes poetry and fiction, teaches writing groups and leads a Dorset Stanza group. Her poems have appeared in anthologies and magazines including *The Frogmore Papers*, *The Interpreter's House*, collections from Templar Poetry and the Emma Press, and online on the Poetry Society website. Poems for children have featured in various places, including *The Caterpillar*. Sarah often writes about relationships, and has particular interests in psychological, social and environmental issues. Among the prizes won by her poems are first in the Frogmore Poetry Prize 2015 and the National Memory Day poetry competition 2018, second in the Poetry on the Lake competition 2018, and placed in the Bridport Prize 2010 and 2016.

JULIA BELL is a writer of novels, poetry, screenplays and essays and Course Director of the Creative Writing MA at Birkbeck. Her most recent essays can be found in *The White Review* and the *TLS*, and her most recent novel, *The Dark Light*, is published by Macmillan. She is also co-editor of *The Creative Writing Coursebook* (Macmillan), which was reissued in August 2019. She divides her time between London and Berlin.

M. W. BEWICK grew up on the edge of the Lake District, and now lives in rural Essex. Poetry credits include *The High Window*, *Under the Radar*, *Tempest: An Anthology* (Patrician Press, 2019), *Envoi*, *The Stinging Fly*, *Sentinel Literary Quarterly* and *The Interpreter's House*. His first collection of poetry, *Scarecrow*, was published in 2017 (Dunlin Press). He leads the creative and professional writing programme at LCCM in London, and is co-founder and editor at independent publisher and art project, Dunlin Press.

RACHEL BOWER is a Leverhulme Fellow at the University of Leeds. She is the author of *Moon Milk* (Valley Press, 2018) and *Epistolarity and World Literature, 1980–2010* (Palgrave Macmillan, 2017), and the editor, with Helen Mort, of the *Verse Matters* anthology (Valley Press, 2017). Her poetry has been published widely, including in *Magma*, *Stand*, *New Welsh Reader*, *Frontier* and *Popshot*, and her work has been shortlisted for *The London Magazine* Poetry Prize and *The White Review* Short Story Prize.

SEASON BUTLER is a London-based writer, artist and academic. Her practice centres around intersectionality and narratives of otherness, isolation and the end of the world as a contemporary ontological dilemma. Season's debut novel, *Cygnet*, was published by Dialogue Books (UK) and Harper Collins (US) in spring 2019.

CAROL CAFFREY is an Irish writer and actor who lives in Shrewsbury. She writes poetry and short fiction and has been published in a number of journals and anthologies, including *Poetry Ireland Review*, *Lunch Ticket*, *The Ogham Stone*, *Pushing Out the Boat* and *Bare Fiction*. She has been short-listed or placed in several competitions including Fish Flash Fiction, the Allingham Arts Festival, Gettysburg Poets in Parks Residency and the Verve Poetry Festival. She tours the one-woman play *Music for Dogs*, by distinguished Irish poet and playwright Paula Meehan, which earned 4-star reviews at the Edinburgh Fringe.

VALENTINE CARTER became a woman after successfully completing many years as a girl. She recently finished the MA in creative writing at Birkbeck, University of London, where she is now studying for a PhD. Valentine has short fiction published by *The Fiction Pool*, *Bandit Fiction*, *In Yer Ear* and in *The Mechanics' Institute Review*, Issue 15.

JUDY DARLEY is a British fiction writer, poet and journalist who can't stop writing about the fallibilities and strengths of the human mind. Her writing has been published by magazines and anthologies in the UK, New Zealand, US and Canada, including *Mslexia*, *Unthology 8* and *SmokeLong Quarterly*, as well as in her debut short-story collection *Remember Me To The Bees* (Scopophilia, 2014). Valley Press will publish her second collection, *Sky Light Rain*, in November 2019. She has shared her stories on BBC radio, as well as in cafés, caves, an artist's studio and a disused church. Find Judy at http://www.SkyLightRain.com and https://twitter.com/JudyDarley.

REENA DENNHARDT left England to become a Citizen of Nowhere. She spent twenty years working in finance, mainly with technology companies but also in German football and Italian fashion. She is currently studying for an MA in creative writing at Birkbeck. Life has made her a strong believer in pragmatism, graft and deadlines. She suspects novel-writing is the closest she'll ever come to experiencing rapture. Reena tends to write tales set in the near future. Her recently completed first novel (crime/sci-fi) is anchored in the Silicon Valley preoccupations of today. Twitter: Reo@Reodennhardt.

K. M. ELKES lives in the West Country. His debut flash fiction collection, *All That Is Between Us*, was published in June 2019 (Ad Hoc Fiction). His short stories have won, or been placed in, a number of international writing competitions, including the Manchester Fiction Prize, the Fish Publishing Prize, the Bridport Prize and the *Aesthetica* Creative Writing Award. His work has appeared in more than 30 anthologies and literary journals, including *The Lonely Crowd*, *Unthology*, *Short Fiction Journal* and *Structo*. As a writer from a rural working-class background, his work reflects marginalised voices and liminal places. He is currently working on a novel and a short-story cycle.

DIEGO FERRARI is an artist and photographer. Born in Argentina, he studied fine art at Escola Llotja in Barcelona and at Goldsmiths, University of London, and art and architecture at the University of Kent. He teaches at Elisava University in Barcelona, Central Saint Martins and Goldsmiths, and is Senior Lecturer in photography at Kingston University. He has held artist's residencies in China, Germany, Guatemala, Romania, Hungary and Estonia, and his work has been exhibited widely around the world. His recent work interrogates the relationship between social values and public spaces, with a particular interest in the dynamic between the body and the built and natural environment.

RONAN FITZGERALD is a Dubliner living in London. A former BBC journalist, he recently completed an MA in creative writing at Birkbeck and will begin studying for an MFA in October 2019. He has a diploma in drama from the Royal Central School of Speech and Drama and his writing for the stage has been funded by Arts Council England. He is working on a collection of short stories and a found poetry pamphlet. "The Girl in the Orange Dress" is his first published poem.

RICHARD HAMBLYN's books include *The Invention of Clouds* (Picador, 2001), which won the 2002 *Los Angeles Times* Book Prize; *Terra: Tales of the Earth* (Picador, 2009), a study of natural disasters, and *The Art of Science* (Picador, 2011), an anthology of readable science writing from the Babylonians to the Higgs boson. His most recent book, *Clouds: Nature and Culture*, was published in 2017 (Reaktion), and he is currently working on a companion volume about the art and science of the sea. He is Programme Director of Birkbeck's BA Creative Writing.

EMILY HINSHELWOOD is a poet, playwright, tutor and performer. She has edited two climate change poetry anthologies, and produced plays responding to the theme. She is poet-in-residence at climate change conferences in the UK and Europe and co-founded the largest windfarm cooperative in Wales. She has been running arts and climate change events and workshops for many years. She was a lecturer in anthropology and sustainable development at Swansea University, and is co-author of the research report "Culture Shift: How Artists are responding to Sustainability in Wales". She teaches writing to adults, young people and children, and recently walked through Wales asking everyone she met "three questions on climate change".

EMMA HUTTON is an Irish writer based in London. She won the Mairtín Crawford Short Story Award 2019, the final TSS Flash Fiction 400 competition in spring 2019, was placed third in the TSS Cambridge Short Story Prize 2018, received a special mention in the Galley Beggar Press Short Story Prize 2018/19, was highly commended in the London Short Story Prize 2018 and shortlisted for the 2018 Seán O'Faoláin International Short Story Prize. Her stories have appeared in *Litro* and *Southword*. She is working on her first short-story collection.

LAWRENCE ILLSLEY is a Cornish poet based in the Welsh Valleys. He is studying for an MA in creative writing at Birkbeck, University of London, specialising in poetry. His long narrative poem *Astra and Sebastian* was shortlisted for the International Proverse Prize and subsequently published (Proverse, 2017), and his short pieces have featured in *Shooter* and *Ariadne's Thread* magazines. He is currently working on a new narrative poem called *A Brief History of Trees in England and Wales*, about trees, the ecology of place and movement, and the loss of his parents, themes that often recur in his work.

TARQUIN LANDSEER graduated from Royal Holloway, University of London, with an MA in poetry and poetics. He is the recipient of a Keats-Shelley Memorial Association Prize, and in 2016 won first prize in the International Welsh Poetry Competition. Various poems have appeared in *The Keats-Shelley Review*, *Staple* and *The Frogmore Papers*, and in the anthologies *Peloton* by Templar Poetry, *Bedford Square 10* and *Humanagerie*. His poetry tends to engage with invisible boundaries, different states of consciousness, liminal zones of perception, the otherness of animals, and the interface between the human and the non-human, often as a means of eliciting imaginative empathy.

ANDREW LEACH is a writer of novels, poetry and short stories. At fifteen, he went to work for Paul Raymond and is currently writing a novel based on the experience. His first novel, *Blow Your Kiss Hello* (Angel and Nightingale Press, 2012), was published under the name Andrew James, a temporary pseudonym adopted for reasons of secrecy that remain unrelated to spying. His fiction has been published by several presses, and his poetry has featured in *Strix* and *Magma Poetry*. He has completed two more novels, one of which is rumoured to be "quite good". He lives – mainly in the 1970s – in Wandsworth, south-west London.

A keen traveller and environmental enthusiast from Atherstone in the middle of the Midlands, **LAURA LEWIS-WATERS** has lived in four countries on three continents, leaving behind poetry and travel writing in all three. Combining travel with education, she has studied English literature, history, creative writing and volcanology across five different universities. Laura is currently teaching English at a secondary school whilst completing research for a PhD, which is focused on using verbatim poetry and maps to (re)present voices affected by sea level rise.

FRAN LOCK is an associate poetry editor at Culture Matters and author of five poetry collections: *Ruses and Fuses* (Culture Matters, 2018), *Muses and Bruises* (Manifesto Press, 2017), *Dogtooth* (Out-Spoken Press, 2017), *The Mystic and the Pig Thief* (Salt, 2014) and *Flatrock* (Little Episodes, 2011). Her next collection, *Contains Mild Peril*, is forthcoming from Out-Spoken Press later this year. She is currently undertaking a practice-based PhD at Birkbeck in contemporary poetry.

SHAUNA MACKAY's work has most recently been published, or is forthcoming, with *The Weekend Read*, *New Ohio Review*, *Ambit* and *Phantom Drift*.

JEAN MCNEIL is the author of fourteen books, including six novels, a collection of short fiction, a collection of poetry, a travel guide and literary essays. She has undertaken official residencies in Antarctica; the Falkland Islands; in Svalbard, Norway; and aboard a NERC-funded expedition to Greenland. *Ice Diaries: An Antarctic Memoir* (ECW Press) won the Grand Prize at the Banff Mountain Film Festival Book Competition in 2016, and was selected by the *Guardian* as one of the best nature books of 2018. Her most recent novel is *Fire on the Mountain* (Legend Press, 2018). She is Reader in Creative Writing and Director of the creative-critical PhD programme at the University of East Anglia.

KATE NOAKES' seventh and most recent collection of poetry is *The Filthy Quiet* (Parthian, 2019). Her website (boomslangpoetry.blogspot.com) is archived by the National Library of Wales. She lives in London where she acts as a trustee for literature advocacy organisation Spread the Word.

ALEXANDRA PETROPOULOS is a journalist, comedian, editor and musician – she's foreign, so stealing only one of your jobs wasn't enough. Originally from mid-west America she moved to the UK ten years ago. She has recently completed the creative writing MA at Birkbeck, a degree she'll proudly add to the growing pile of impractical qualifications that already includes a BM in flute performance and an MA in ethnomusicology. When she's not writing weird stories about trees falling in love, Alexandra is the deputy editor at the music magazine *Songlines*. Her journalism has appeared in *Songlines*, the *Guardian* and *Wanderlust*, among others.

CARMEL SHORTALL grew up in Northern Ireland and now lives in London. She returned to study after 20 years in local government, completing an MA in creative writing at Birkbeck in 2018. She co-edited Issue 12 of *The Mechanics' Institute Review* and was also part of the editorial team for Birkbeck's Writers' Hub from 2012 to 2014. A lover of books and an occasional bookseller, she has worked for the Big Green Bookshop in Wood Green and since it closed has been involved in setting up a cooperative bookshop and event space to replace it.

JOSHUA SOUTHERN is a writer from Lancashire. He recently completed his master's in creative writing at Sheffield Hallam University, where he also achieved first-class honours in the creative writing BA. He writes mainly fantasy, science fiction and horror, though he has also explored both realist and surrealist drama, the thriller genre and poetry. Most of his writing contains environmentalist undertones, and often has a strong focus on mental health. He splits his time largely between completing his debut novel, the first in a high-fantasy series, and walking his three Labradors.

DAVE WAKELY is one of the organisers of Milton Keynes Lit Fest and of the Lodestone Poets. Shortlisted for the Manchester Fiction Prize 2017 and the Bath Short Story Award 2019, his short stories have appeared in *Ambit*, *Glitterwolf*, *Prole*, *Shooter*, *Token*, previous issues of *The Mechanics' Institute Review* and the anthology *Best Gay Stories 2017* (Lethe Press), amongst other publications. He lives in Buckinghamshire with his husband and a growing collection of books, CDs and guitars, and tweets as @theverbalist.

RUSHIKA WICK is a London-based writer currently studying at the Poetry School. She has an interest in exploring how social contracts and conditions become embodied. She has had contributions in magazines including *Ambit*, *Litro*, *DASH*, *Cold Lips*, *Rx Magazine* and *Allegro* and forthcoming in *3:AM Magazine* and *Flock*. Her work has been included in anthologies such as *Word-O-Mat* Edition 2 and the *New River Press Yearbook 2019* and is forthcoming in *Alter Egos* (Bad Betty Press). Rushika has performed at the Vurige Tongen Poetry Festival in Amsterdam and at various salons/nights in London. She co-hosts the Bad Slide Projector poetry salon.

KATIE WILLIS was a ballet dancer. She now lives in west London, close to a river, dividing her time between water and land, home and hospital. Her fiction is often about women and water. In her creative non-fiction she is currently active claiming autonomy for the patient by rewriting patienthood. Her short stories have been published online in the *Puffin Review* Fairy Tale Competition (2014) and in the anthology *Flamingo Land and Other Stories* (Flight Press, 2015). Having just completed an MA in creative writing at Birkbeck, University of London, Katie is about to begin an MFA.

LORRAINE WILSON spent many years working as a conservation biologist in remote corners of the world, but now lives by the sea in Scotland where she writes stories that are touched by folklore and the wilderness. She has published short stories and creative non-fiction in various anthologies and magazines, and tweets @raine_clouds about science, writing, cats, and – when she can't stop herself – political rage.